MW00605805

BOOM: The Baby Boomers Guide to
Leveraging Technology, so that you can
Preserve Your Independent Lifestyle &
Thrive

# BOOM: The Baby Boomers Guide to Leveraging Technology, so that you can Preserve Your Independent Lifestyle & Thrive

*LISA M. CINI*

BOOM: The Baby Boomers Guide to Leveraging Technology, so that you can Preserve Your Independent Lifestyle & Thrive Copyright © by Lisa M. Cini. All Rights Reserved.

# Contents

# Free and Frequent Updates!

**7-Time #1 Best Selling Author**

**Free and Frequent Updates!**

I am updating this book frequently with more value, interviews, resources, and information based on the feedback you share. I would love to meet and chat with you about any new or amazing tech that you use that I may not have in the book.

If you are reading this book on a Kindle App, please make sure it's the latest version of the book.

To get the latest and greatest, just open your app, click or press the "More" icon in the lower right-hand corner, and then press "Sync", and you will always be updated with the most recent version.

To my tribe, thank you for believing in me and not letting me rest before my mission is complete.

Please go to **www.LisaMCini.com** to sign up for my blog and new exciting stuff.

Please go to **www.bestlivingtech.com** for products that will help you to age in place.

Please go to **www.mosaicdesignstudio.com** to see beautiful engaging senior living homes.

"Latest surveys reveal Baby Boomers are more scared of being unable to care for themselves than they are of dying."

BOOM: *The Baby Boomers Guide to Leveraging Technology, so that you can Preserve Your Independent Lifestyle & Thrive* is filled with key insights and actions to live a safer and less stressful life while saving tens of thousands per year. The book outlines how to leverage the latest state-of-the-art technologies to facilitate aging in the right place and traveling with freedom while also accounting for the challenges of aging (e.g. declining memory, vision impairment, etc.).

# 1. Introduction

As we start this journey together, I need to confess that this book is written out of frustration. It's a typical response from an entrepreneur. When I can't find a solution to a problem, I create the solution. The solution to the problem culminates in a clear, thorough but not overwhelming guide book that will help you successfully age on your own terms.

Imagine never being introduced to silverware, dishes and drinking glasses. You go through life eating with your hands and cupping your hands to drink water (there are no drinking fountains either), you survive but you don't thrive. Life is just much harder because you don't have the proper tools to handle the simple tasks of daily living. Then someone introduces you to silverware and teaches you how to use it. Life is much better but eating soup and drinking is still a messy time-consuming proposition. You have some tools but have not been exposed to the ones that can really impact your life.

This guide book is intended to not only expose you to the best tools out there to age on your own terms but is set up for you to know what you should use when. Imagine eating soup with a fork......it would not be very helpful right? Unfortunately, the information that you and I have been provided regarding technology is a lot like discovering a lost kings tomb from a highly advanced society where we are guessing as to what this or that is for, and we are overwhelmed by the shiny gold everywhere. We might guess right but it can be exhausting trying to analyze all that's out there and understand what will be useful or not.

Having said all this, I bet you'll be surprised to know that this book–the one that you're reading right now, that you bought thinking is all about technology – is actually a book that's all about freedom. We can't stop the clock, but we can stop our limiting beliefs on aging. When we embrace aging on our terms, we become free.

As you enter a new season of your life, I believe that there's a key out there. This key will not only let you unlock the gifts and talents that you'll take with you in this season, but it will also support you all the way through it. That key? Just like in the *Raiders of the Lost Ark* is Technology, but this time it's not ancient technology of a world forgotten, its available to us right now, today! Ultimately, it's what will let you age on your own terms.

Think of BOOM as your own treasure map. It's tying together all the systems, ideas and advancements, and showing you what works with what, and giving you simple, clear information that will help you to decide what works for you in your life.

To be clear, there's no one out there who's really doing this. Vendors aren't very helpful because it's in their best interest if you buy their whole package. Then a little later it's still in their best interest, and not *yours*, if you buy their whole new, newer, newest package. And so very quickly every tech-related item becomes very overcomplicated or outdated.

But it doesn't have to be. Simplification is possible. **BOOM** is simplification! And with it, you'll discover the tech tools to bring you to the best living you can possibly have as you age. My hope is that *knowing* the tools that are out there will let you create smart strategies, and those strategies are what will put you in command of something I feel is critical to aging the way you want to: *making decisions yourself before someone else makes them for you.*

Having smart strategies helps you mitigate the aging process. We're all aging and will continue to age, if we are lucky enough, and the loss of our personal freedom, or if you want to call it something else, call it – the loss of our independence – often comes with the gift of aging. The gift of aging is being old enough to not care what others think and live on our own terms. Smart strategies lessen the loss of personal freedoms that we spent years earning. Some of the strategies are quite simple: a memory rescue diet can help you avoid becoming memory impaired and having a personal assistant robot can keep you on track with your schedule and remind you to take your medications. Technology makes both easier, helping you track your memory diet and keeping you out of the hospital by not letting you forget to take your blood pressure pills is just the tip of the iceberg.

If you want to go the route of aging in a "home," technology can aid in your understanding of which of those homes will be the best fit for you. Freedom is making the choice yourself, so you don't have it made for you and end up living out your life in a place where you don't feel you belong.

Where health decisions are concerned, **BOOM** explains how using technology moves you away from being reactive and towards being proactive. We'll look at A.I. (Artificial Intelligence), Data Mining and Sensors and how they can help you accomplish that. Stay with me on this journey and this book will take both of those terms and make them feel like your familiar friends, as opposed to your scary science fiction, dystopian future nightmare.

For the last 20 years, I've been the CEO of the Mosaic Design Studio, one of the country's largest senior living design firms, so as you can imagine, I've spent a lot of time thinking about the topic of how we age. I've thought about aging from the 30,000-foot macro perspective, and from an extremely up close and micro perspective. I've talked to the owners and developers of senior living facilities; I've been inspired by the leading thinkers in the field of aging; I've had moving conversations about the topic from people in the thick of it; and finally, I've experienced it in the most personal and intimate ways. For the last few years, I've been living my life in the middle of my family's "social experiment" where we have 4 generations living under one roof, and the eldest generation is my 96-year-old grandmother, who deals with (and so we *all* deal with) Alzheimer's/Dementia.

What I've learned from all of this is that you can only have freedom if:

- What are my technology options?)
- What do I need right now, what do I have access to right now, what do I anticipate needing in my future?

What else helps is knowing your personal definition of retirement. My old buddy Webster defines it like this: "*To withdraw from use or service, to take out of use.*"

But is that how you define it? Do you feel that when you retire you're done contributing? Do you think, "*That's it, now I'll just sit on the front porch, in my rocker, until I die?* Or, will you choose to see your gifts and talents, and use them to redefine your life in this new season?

"*Plant your seeds before you need the harvest*" is a quote

that rings true as we are discussing freedom. Wisdom to me, is planning that *you* determine is best for you today so that you won't be dealing with crisis management in the future. I've seen crisis management from close up; it's never easy, never pretty and rarely brings happiness to anyone involved. No matter where you are in your season, you are ahead of where you would be if you had not taken the time to read BOOM. It will serve you well.

So, let's plant some seeds and make our harvest one that's beautiful and self-determined.

# 2. Laying the Groundwork

The world is changing faster than we know at exponential speeds in all directions. It's exciting but a little scary, kind of like your first kiss, roller coaster ride or learning to drive a car. Looking back, it was always worth it. It's what makes me know I am alive. Let's start with what I'll call **The Big 3**. These big questions will be framing the conversation, pretty much any conversation, this book takes on.

1. How are you going to be able to live your life with freedom and confidence?

2. Will you be living your life?

3. How are you going to care for your mind, body, and spirit?

**1. HOW ARE YOU GOING TO BE ABLE TO LIVE YOUR LIFE WITH FREEDOM AND CONFIDENCE?**

This is all about technology. Technology is any tool that makes our lives easier. Hunting tools were created long, long ago so we could eat. Then we created more tools, called "nets," so we could expand our diets and eat fish. And now we have created another new kind of "net" tool, the *Internet*. Once again, technology has given us a tool to make our lives easier. Technology isn't limited to the things that we have to plug into the wall. Technology is all around us.

Technology's nothing new. As human beings we have a drive to create things and technology is our way to fulfill this drive. My goal in my professional career, and with this book, is to merge our drive to create with our process of aging. Because if that happens technology will let us age gracefully (whenever possible!), on our own terms, and enjoying life up to our last moment.

## 2. WHERE WILL YOU BE LIVING YOUR LIFE?

This question is one that's about *Health Care* vs. *Well Care*. You don't want to be sent to a "prison," do you? And yes, "prison" is exactly the way I've heard a lot of people describe their idea of "senior homes." Now don't get me wrong, at my firm Mosaic Design Studio we design beautiful award-winning senior living homes that are like the Ritz, but the statistics say that 90% of US seniors still don't want to live in senior living no matter how beautiful my team and I make it. Senior living is a lot like sushi, it's not for everyone, but for those that enjoy it, it's expensive but wonderful. Are you in the 90% or the 10%?

But if you're a boomer, the chances are good that you've been living your life right *where you want to live it*. And chances are also good that no one's told you where (or how) to live it before, so why in the world would you start letting them tell you where to live it *now*?

And probably, you don't want them to tell you. Most likely *you* want to remain the one who's driving/steering your life bus, and that makes sense. But there's also a chance that as you look around today, you're seeing choices regarding your "where" that don't seem like you at all.

That's because they're not.

Those choices were right for the "*silent generation*," the people who were born from around 1925-1945. Their choices look like: Home Health, Independent Living (IL,) Assisted Living (AL,) Memory Care (MC,) and SN: Skilled Nursing. That was then, this is now.

Your choices are way more flexible but can seem more complex. Imagine their flexibility like women's fashion today. It used to be you could tell the year by the length of a skirt. If you had a mini skirt on and the fashion of that time was to be below the knee you would not fit in very well.

Aging used to be like this with a very siloed view of where you were allowed to live, depending on your age and your health needs. But as with women's skirts, you can now wear anything you want. Thank gosh as those skirts right below the knee cut me at the worst possible place and made me look shorter than I already am at 4'11" and 10 lbs heavier! Now with Home Healthcare, telemedicine, crowdsourcing and personalized medicine you have tons of options and whatever you choose you don't have to be locked into a lifelong decision. So as your needs change you can change, where and what you want.

## 3. HOW ARE YOU GOING TO CARE FOR YOUR MIND, BODY AND SPIRIT?

Healthcare is about the body only, and that's fine, we all have bodies and they absolutely need care. But what about the rest of what makes us who we are? What about our minds? What about souls?

That's a whole other part of what I mean when I say *"aging on your own terms."* It's looking at all of what you can do, and want to do, for your body, mind, and spirit. Put them all together and you've got a whole, full, real person. Take them apart and it all starts to unravel.

Lucky for us there are tools that keep us together. We will be looking at not only the physical needs of our body with sensors, data mining and personalized supplements, fitness programs and medicines but we will also be looking into the power of connection, adding value, meditation, brain scans and brain food and what drives your spirit or passion that keeps you engaged, resilient and happy.

With the recent advances in personalized medicine, AI,

nanotechnology and us all being connected, the experts are saying that if you can survive the next ten years you can break the 120-year mark or even longer. When this happens a mind shift takes place. Imagine for a moment the age you think you will live too, now what if I could guarantee you would live another 50 years? How would this change your thoughts on how you would take care of your mind, body, and spirit. Would you write that book you always wanted to leave Wall Street and go back to school and become a teacher? What legacy would you want to leave by living a full life and giving to all those you know and love with your gifts and talents? This might seem like a big bomb to drop but it's happening, and as I mentioned before wisdom is creating a plan before the crisis.

The speed at which technology is improving and can be completely overwhelming. But, it also gives us almost unlimited options and autonomy in deciding how we want to live and how we want to age. Just think about how quickly we went from no cell phones to huge, bulky cell phones, to phones that fit in your pocket and now we have access to the entire world.

We now have access to so many things and while the ride is fast, it is worth exploring how it can help us keep our freedom, keep us safe, and keep us healthy.

# 3. Technology and The Kid Connection

Kids don't care about technology in terms of its social aspects, its barriers or the issues that might be wrapped up in it. What they care about is whether or not it serves them. If it does, they'll tell everyone about it; they'll preach loud, clear and forever. American Idol? Yeah, its success was largely due to 'Tween girls. Twilight? Yep, pretty much the same demographic, 8-12 or 9-13 (depending on the resource) years old in case you were wondering what a tween was like I was. Tweens have an estimated spending power of 200 billion, that's BILLION. And if a specific technology doesn't serve them? They'll quit it and adopt something new.

Take for example the iPhone, the percentage of tweens with an iPhone was 76% for tween girls but is dropping to 53%. When the iPhone first emerged, it quickly became a fashion statement. Fashion is something that always grabs the younger generation first. But as time marched on, the iPhone is no longer the fashion statement, but has become a tool. As a tool, it does not create the same need-to-have feeling as when it was a fashion statement. As a tool, there are more options to work with between Android and Windows phones.

In my work, I look at what kids are doing, what they're adopting, and think about how maybe those things could help Boomers, as they move forward and make decisions about the future. My reasoning for this is that if a kid can use it, then its intuitive. They typically don't whip out a user manual and start reading from Step 1. If the product is not useful they will discard it and it will die a quick cold death and be buried in the technology graveyard, but if it is a winner in their eyes like Google, Facebook, Instagram, DoorDash, Uber and Instagram then I am willing to get on the bus and figure out how to use the tech tool to make my life better. You can count on one thing with kids and technology, they NEVER adopt technology that makes their life harder. They are brand agnostic and value driven. They are the best, cheapest research team we've got, and we just have to watch and wait.

What do kids use? They have tablets and smartphones that parents put into their hands to entertain them, let them collaborate with others, and also to communicate with friends. What do Boomers use? A tablet (iPad) or smartphone for entertainment, collaboration, and communication. It's amazing the similarities.

What's the next tech that the kids are using, and we need to leverage? 3D printing and Augmented Reality / Virtual Reality (AR/VR).

To explain VR (Virtual Reality) is like being inside of a

dream or a video game. You do not have full movement, but you are experiencing the situation you are seeing through goggles that are connected to a computer. The scientific data states that if you are placed in a scary/horror VR environment your body will react in a stressed way, but if you are placed into a happy VR environment...you will react in a happy, no-stressed way. Virtual Reality (VR) is being used to help those with PTSD that were in the military and people with phobias. They are using the technology to reduce stress to that situation until it's all gone. Likewise, being in a happy situation makes you happier. Imagine being in a peaceful scene (your favorite vacation spot) and you can go there whenever you put on the goggles or sculpting in 3D right in your living room without having to get all supplies ready or clean up afterward.

Augmented reality is similar, but it adds to glasses you already wear (with an adapter) to help you see items that may be of benefit, for example when you are in your kitchen and you look at the refrigerator it may remind you that you are out of milk. if you have ever watched a professional football game on tv, they use augmented reality to superimpose the lines on the field to show where the first down has to be. These tools are a blend of entertainment, education and having a 24/7 personal assistant.

It may sound crazy to you now, but imagine driving on a

trip without GPS. Eventually, these tech tools will become so integrated into our lives, they will seem as necessary as indoor plumbing or electric lights.

It's an exciting place to be, right here, right now, leveraging the past and the present and peeking into the future.

This may come off like I am a geek or nerd, but it's critical to "geek out" a little bit so that you can fully understand the changes coming. If we can successfully hang around for the next 10 years, the positive exponential world changes will be larger than we could ever imagine for our lives and health.

When I say the word exponential, what I mean is a huge shift in our reality. Think of it like this, when you have one child you deal with the issues of having that one child, its challenging but manageable. Millions of people throughout time have done it. Now think about having twins, it's not earth shatter, but the work doubles and you have to modify your plans and maybe even get some help. I remember my cousin having twins and just feeding them was quite the challenge, her mother and husband helped because it was more than a 24-hour job keeping the twins satisfied. Now let's move to an exponential change, 10 kids...... at one time. Basically, a human litter. What worked in the past will no longer work. A completely new strategy has to be implemented. You probably would have to get a new car, house, and definitely would have to enlist assistance or help from others. Just think of feeding time and trying to handle feeding 10 babies at once, it's impossible and even if you developed skills like those circus performers where you got the plates spinning in the air, all at the same time and ran back and forth making sure that one did not drop, eventually you would tire out and something would fall.

Now imagine that but in a positive way, the exponential is not about having to do more things and run from plate to plate, hoping that nothing will fall and break but its exponential change that allows computers, robots, teams to anticipate your needs before you even see them and help you handle what used to be a chore or very difficult. This type of change creates not just an evolution, it creates and revolution.

The best way to explain it is if you could go back to the US prior to home appliances. Washing your clothes required capturing rainwater, then using a washing board or paddle contraption that you had to turn to agitate the mixture of water, lye and clothes to clean them and then rinsing the clothes and then finally hanging them on the clothesline to dry. Cooking that needed to be completed required a garden (let's not even go into that effort), getting fuel for the stove, starting the fire, gathering the eggs, preparing the bread, food etc. and then cooking and then cleaning the dishes and then starting all over again.

Then let's move onto sweeping the floors and rugs, not an easy task. Rugs would need to be removed from under the furniture dragged outside, hung on a line or fence and have the dirt beat out of them and then drug back into the house and the furniture moved back onto them. There is also this little thing about having to light all the lamps in the house and deal with no indoor plumbing (In most cases, until the 1930's in rural American indoor plumbing and electric did not exist) so unless you were living in NYC, Chicago or Philly, a bowl for washing your face and a chamber pot were your bathroom in your house. Of course, if you were rich enough to have domestic servants none of this would have mattered to you.

Taking care of your home was such a chore prior to household appliances that my grandmothers (she's 96) school book on Foods and Home Making by Greer 1928 had a whole section in the Modern Housewifery chapter on Stoves and Fire building! It explained wood and coal ranges and the supply of air needed and more. Basically, she was an expert in HVAC (Heating, Ventilation and Air Conditioning) for her family. Making sure they were comfortable, well fed and the home was clean and functioning properly.

Move forward to when appliances started to become mainstream, the Hoover Vacuum cleaner was one appliance that started being sold in 1908 and touted that "it beats...as it sweeps...as it cleans" it was an amazing time and back saver.

In the 1930s things changed due to a government program called the REA or Rural Electrification Administration, that's goal was to bring electricity to the rural areas of the US. Instead of heating an iron on your coal or wood stove you could now just plug it in and voila! It was heated, no more starting a fire, stoking it and then heating the iron. Time was being won back for the modern housewife of the late 1930s.

Now let's think about kids and how their interaction with technology has created new opportunities. Entertainment is one of the top areas of growth and much of it aims to please a younger demographic. We went from listening to the radio to TVs in every home. This made way for Saturday morning cartoons that everyone remembers fondly. The next step was computers for commercial use. Think about how quickly computers expanded once they became used for more than just business processing but could be used for games and programs for kids. Now we've gone from computers to tablets where we can bring everything with us in our backpack from spreadsheets to games to Netflix (online movies). And the newest jump has been the use of Augmented Reality (AR). The games created under the AR platforms are only getting better which means they are always becoming more useful and educational.

To understand the past and the present in technology you need to understand Moore's Law and its impact on exponential growth. Moore's Law basically states that computing power doubles every 24 months. Peter Diamandis presents the following data in his book *Abundance*: "In 1971, the Intel 4004 integrated circuit had 2,300 transistors costing $1 each with .00074GHz of processing power. Today, an Nvidia GPU has over 7.1 billion transistors, which cost less than $0.0000001 each and has over 7GHz of processing power. This is 10,000 times faster, 10 million times cheaper, and 100 billion-fold improvement." This explains how computers can get smaller and smaller yet be faster and smarter. It is said that a kid in Africa with a smartphone has more technology than President Bill Clinton had at his disposal when in office. Everything we use that has a computer in it has been impacted by Moore's Law.

Take a moment and make a list, either mentally or on a piece of paper, of all of the technology you currently use on a daily basis. Given the definition that technology is the application of scientific knowledge for practical purposes, what do you come up with? In a couple of seconds, I came up with over 45 technologies that I use on a daily basis, and I did not include software or apps. If I had, I am sure the list would have been twice as long.

1. Phone
2. Cell phone
3. Car
4. Electric curling iron
5. Sonic toothbrush
6. Hair dryer
7. Indoor plumbing
8. Alarm system
9. GPS
10. Cloud computing
11. Laptop computer
12. Tablet
13. Digital camera
14. Fax
15. Copier
16. Vacuum sweeper
17. Clothes washer
18. Clothes dryer
19. Dishwasher
20. Refrigerator
21. Electric auto-dimming lighting
22. Heated flooring
23. Thermostats to electric heat
24. Gas hot water tank
25. Blender
26. Juicer
27. Stove
28. Oven

29. Microwave
30. Coffee pot
31. Food Processor
32. Electric bed
33. Massage chair
34. Scooter
35. Personal printer
36. Glasses
37. Electric iron
38. Safety cameras on car
39. Heated electric bidet/toilet
40. WiFi
41. TV
42. Alexa / Google Home
43. DVR/DVD
44. Outlook calendar
45. WiFi speakers

These technologies are average to most consumers, the point is when you were growing up could you ever have imagined having a microwave in your kitchen, a printer in your home office and a cell phone? It would have been impossible then to dream up the technology let alone understand how it would change our lives for the (mostly) better.

Technologies that we are dealing with in the present that should be leveraged by the baby boomers are those that impact your ability to live your life with freedom and confidence.

In designing for thousands of senior living homes over the past 25 years and visiting many more, I am still shocked by the lack of technologies used to make the environment better, cheaper and more connected. It seems there is a distrust of technology that being connected or watched will open a potential for lawsuits and make it even harder to provide care for seniors and stay profitable. Dignity is the other factor that gets brought up as a stumbling block to adopting new technology in senior living. The key is appropriate permission-based use of technology. Great technology is hardly noticeable, as you will see, and it solves problems that improve dignity, safety, outcomes, compliance, and risk. It's like adding in the seat belt to cars back in 1984, at first it felt restrictive but then it was comforting to know you would not fly through the window if, God forbid you were in an accident.

The easiest way to approach this discussion will have to be twofold. First, you need to define your categories of technology that you will need, and then second, these technologies will need to be married to the impact they have on how you want to live your life. Basically, the cost of the technology both in dollars and change has to outweigh the pain of doing things the old way.

*Typically, technology is first adapted by those with the lowest mental barriers to using it. Tweens and teens usually fit the bill. When I was having trouble doing research on the Internet in 1998 I asked the 9-year-old neighbor kid to help. He told me to type in the word "Google". I said, "Google? What is it?" He told me, just do it and stop asking questions.*

Technology does require an investment, and this is usually the first and largest objection. But I ask you, can you imagine using an outhouse versus indoor plumbing? Having to use a pail to get your water out of your well to get your water vs. turning the lever on your sink? It sounds ridiculous to us now. The amount of time wasted in villages without running water keeps girls from being educated, not to mention the safety issues involved. Can you imagine going back to a non-electric typewriter? I can't comprehend how long and how many rewrites it would take me to write what you're reading.

Or let's go a step further. Let's say you have access to

the Internet but you choose not to use the technology because it's silly, with all the Facebook stuff and the costs to have it. Now imagine you need to research something, so you go to the library (yes, they still exist), and you search through the system to find out which books may be of value. You then get their Dewey Decimal numbers and you're off on a hunt. The books are all over the library and intermixed. They're heavy, but that means value, right? You then look at each one, looking for a hidden treasure of evidence; finally, you find your nuggets. When the information is short, you hand-copy it down but when it's large you mark the page and then copy it at the copier. After all the research is completed you have to return the books. If you missed something and can't remember which book it came from, you have to start all over. There is no cookie history to lead you back to where you were. This was exhausting to write; just detailing it out felt like a waste of time, yet some baby boomers are very much like what I have just described, using archaic systems because they exist and are familiar. My mother-in-law won't get on Facebook and complains that she's not as connected to the kids as she would like, she has internet and instant access if she chooses but feels it silly and is stuck in her old ways. My mother on the other hand at 78 is very connected, she Facebooks, Instagrams, Snapchats with her grandkids and keeps a very open real-time up to date relationship with them. They both have the same access to the same tools, one just chooses not to move into the future and use them.

Let's go back to the library scenario, just recently Google introduced a book search called *Talk to Books* that allows you to search millions of books in a second. Not just the title, but every word in all of these books for exactly for what you are searching for. Just as the Dewey Decimal system allowed us to save time then, this newest google searching technology will make things even faster and more accurate. Millennials will be able to say to their kids... "back in my day, Google only gave you book titles, we still had to read all those books...."

The point is, we can't imagine the future but we can be mentally prepared to take advantage of it. Talk to your grandkids or neighbor kids about what they are using and how it may help you. Have fun with this, you're not going to break anything.

Technology can help you to increase your quality of life and freedom.

# 4. You've Heard of the 6 Senses, but Have You Heard of the 6 D's?

Understanding Peters 6 D'S of Tech Disruption: Digitize, Deceptive, Disruptive, Demonetize, Dematerialize, Democratize will help you find your footing in the world of technology. He explains in simple terms the seasons of technology so you won't be caught off guard or at the very least you will know the next stage and that there will be a shift happening.

**1. Digitize.**

***The Idea:*** Digitize, anything that becomes digitized becomes disruptive. Think of the when books had to be hand copied and then came along the printing press. All of a sudden books and Bible was given to the masses. Being able to mass distribute information changed the whole world. Now you can carry 10,000 books on your phone or tablet.

Remember back when music could only be heard live? When it was able to be recorded and distributed on an album, people were able to enjoy music where and when they liked and millions more had access to the best musicians in the world.

Photos are another example, when film was developed.

But when they went digital (taking a photo on your phone for example and sending it via your phone to another) how we recorded and shared our lives forever changed and now every moment is captured.

When you digitize, something, books, music, images it allows everyone to have access anywhere at any time.

**Why is this important to you?**

Our medical records and all the testing and imaging are currently being digitized, this will allow Artificial Intelligence and Data mining to help us be our best us by tailoring all our health care into WellCare. Telemedicine will now be possible with everything being digitized which should break the insurance industries locks on how portable our insurance is, this, in turn, will drive down all the healthcare costs. Basically, you will be able to be in control and "own" your music, books, photos and medical records allowing you to travel as you wish with all of your favorite things in your pocket and not having to worry about if you get sick or needing a prescription filled because the local doctor will have immediate access to your entire medical history and even be able to video in your personal doctor for consult if needed all seamlessly.

**2. Deceptive.**

**The Idea:** when it starts being digitized its growth is deceptive. When it starts out its hard to even see its getting traction then the law of compounding comes into play and everyone thinks it's an overnight success but really it's been building and building and then finally light a plane on a runway it takes off.

**Why is this important to you?**

Blockchain and Bitcoin are perfect examples of deceptive. They are digital currency (money that is real, but it is existing only on the internet) that no government can control or tax. Several online retailers will take Bitcoin as payment and it will only get larger, by the time it comes out of deceptive the entire economic system of the world will be changed.

Remember when bank cards started with debit cards. Bitcoin is a new form of money that is universal. Which popular companies like Travelocity takes. We may not understand how it works yet, but the world is moving in a direction to make money easier for us to understand. It will also help us when traveling as your "bitcoin" currency in the future would be like using your credit card now except there is no need to convert the dollars to Euro for example. The bitcoin price would be the same no matter where you are, Africa, Italy, Mexico or the United States.

### 3. Disruptive.

**The Idea:** When digitizing moves from deceptive into disruptive it knocks out the existing technology. Think about how we used to consume music, you would go to the record store and buy it, now you download the music right to your phone and records are considered an antique novelty. Cell phones did the same thing to landline phones, In our house, we do not have a landline, even my parents use only their cellphones.

**Why is this important to you?**

Today, wifi connects us all to the internet and each other anywhere in the world. The local coffee shop, library, beauty salon, and senior living all have wifi because customers are demanding it. The status quo has been disrupted!

This is where we are heading with VR/AR, too, and probably by the time you're reading this, it will have already disrupted life and will be part of the normal, or accepted, way of life.

Remember the Periodic Table of Elements from your High School chemistry days? Remember thinking you'd parted ways...maybe even somewhat amicably? Well who thought it *wasn't* done, and who thought it, like some of its gases, was inactive? I did. But on Dec 2$^{nd}$ 2016, I learned that I was wrong, that's when four new elements were added to it, one was *graphene*. Wondering how this fits into disruptive?

Graphene is an allotrope of carbon. It's also a new kid

on the Periodic Table of Elements block! And it's also 200 times stronger than the strongest steel. In car manufacturing, first, it was, "*Steel, steel, steel.*" And then they realized that aluminum was better. "*Aluminum, aluminum, aluminum.*" Those poor car manufacturers and developers; they just got done retooling everything again, and along comes graphene. Now it's, "Shove over aluminum, here comes graphene."

The key to our future is flexibility. Disruption will continue to happen, faster and faster. This is great for aging, it means that just because something worked in the past doesn't mean that something in the future won't disrupt it and make it even better. While it's not a disruptor yet, some doctors I have spoken to feel that stem cell therapy will be the next disruptor. Imagine getting a couple of knee or hip injections and your body heals itself instead of having to do surgery or rehab! This disruption would be a huge blessing for all of us as we age, increasing our confidence and freedom.

**4. De-monetize.**

*The Idea:* Reaching this "D" means that money is no longer a barrier between the first adapters—or what I'll call "the Richie Riches," and the rest of us normal folk who are now getting it.

**Why is this important to you?**

Remember back to the day of those big clunky, cell phones? If that's not enough to trigger your memory...remember that they had antennae?! Well, back then, only super rich people, maybe a President, and a few Kings had one. Now, little kids in the poorest countries can afford to have as much access as only the elite had before.

When money is no longer an object we've experienced "de-monetization." This means that technology that has reached this point will be super cost effective and improve your life as you age providing you more confidence and freedom.

## 5. Dematerialize.

**The Idea:** We're not carrying a lot of "stuff" anymore.

**Why is this important to you?**

I used to carry a camera, phone, pager, separate GPS, and a Franklin planner (which to this day I still miss!) And, for my work as a designer, I had a level, too! Back then, I'd be carrying 6 or 7 things with me every time I traveled for work. Not anymore; now I have it all on a phone.

When material goods fall to the wayside because they're encompassed by one thing, we've witnessed, "dematerialization." Recently, they are looking at the ear as the new wrist. What I mean by that is that the ear is a great place to measure your balance, brain, and heart. Overlay the fact that most people use earbuds with their phones to listen to podcasts, books on tape, music or have phone calls, the ear becomes the perfect place to measure all of your health data, help you connect and also hear better. Marry this with Augmented Reality (AR) glasses and you can say goodbye to your smartwatches and cell phones. Imagine just wearing a hearing device and glasses to take photos, have access to all of your data and connect, relax and listen to whatever you need.

## 6. Democratize.

**The Idea:** The day comes where everyone can have it; access is open to anybody and available to all. Not too long ago in the getting to use a public toilet (not an outhouse) was not for everyone, as the standards have risen everyone gets access. In other parts of the world, you still have to pay to use the toilet facilities.

### Why is this important to you?

With the rise of the internet and access for anyone, the world is at your fingertips in seconds. What used to be only for the rich and the elite of society is now free to everyone and instantly available.

With Data Mining and AI, you can now invest for yourself, read the latest medical breakthroughs and know what is happening in every part of the world. When you democratize, the best of the best is available to everyone no matter your age or economic standing.

## 7. Delocalization.

Peter has recently introduced a 7th disruption, **Delocalization.** Basically with the all of the 6 D's happening, the world is getting smaller, we can reach anyone anywhere with the above disruptions. We will no longer have boundaries which will open up our life to so much more fullness and aid in technologies to improve our life as we age. To learn more about delocalization please go to Peters website https://www.diamandis.com

## MOORE'S LAW:

**What it is**: Computing power doubles every 24 months.

*Why is it important to you?*

We can't anticipate what comes next. And because of this you have to have to be able to have *future flexibility*, because we don't really know what ideas are going to hit and which ones aren't.

And just to make it a little more complicated, very often something else is going to piggy-back off the new thing and it's going to go pretty far off the charts. We don't know which technology is going to take off, there could be 50 things going...until it reaches the disruptive phase and starts to skyrocket, it's a little bit like playing the stock market.

As I write this I'm thinking that AR (augmented reality) and VR (virtual reality) are going to hit and skyrocket. Have some fun learning about all of these technologies and imagine the positive possible impact on improving your life, then try them out.

# 5. AI, Sensors and Data Mining

Alexa is our personal assistant, personal shopper, DJ, patron saint of lost phones, temperature and light controller, newsman, weatherman, and comedian. The Amazon Echo – Powered by Alexa is the newest member of our family. "Alexa" is the persona you talk to similar to iPhone's "Siri" persona. She is connected to Amazon so she can do more and more each day. I am thinking about getting a Samsung Family Smart Hub refrigerator and if I do, she will be connected to my fridge and help me get groceries. Alexa is a mashup of Rosie the Robot from the Jetsons and Jarvis from Iron Man.

One technology that surrounds you every day, but you may not be aware of is data mining. Facebook and Google use it every day. When you get on the Internet, whether you're aware of this or not, they are targeting you. They are sending you things that you've already looked at so it's specifically targeted toward your likes. Think of it in "old school" terms. If I want to date a certain person, I would find out what food they liked, sports teams, the music they listened too and what movies they liked to see. I would then drop hints about these things to the person I like so that we had a common bond. I would be much more successful in getting a date with this "data". It might keep me from asking them to a steak dinner when they are vegan. Data mining is just collecting data and making it useful. Why see 1000 ads for something you don't care about when data mining can help you see two relating to exactly what you need.

Companies use data mining to learn your behaviors and patterns and reduce the amount of digital noise so that you can purchase and buy from them faster and easier. That's their ultimate goal. If you have recently looked up how to quit smoking, this gets "mined" and then you see ads scrolling on the side of Facebook for e-cigarettes, patches and any other means to help you quit smoking. It's really quite brilliant, but also a little unnerving.

If you have ever stayed at a Four Seasons Hotel, they are known for data mining as a way to improve customer service. It goes something like this: when a guest arrives, they have an idea of when they will be coming. They use clues like a spy would to figure out who they are and, if need be, the bellman will ask their name. The bellman then radios the front desk and lets them know Mr. Smith is coming. The guest is greeted with a warm welcome to the Four Seasons, "Mr. Smith, we're so glad you're staying with us." This process keeps happening throughout the whole stay.

How awesome would it be if your house could be as customer focused as the staff at a Four Seasons Hotel? As I have mentioned previously, please remember, not all technology involves fancy space-age computers; some technology that we already have access to just needs to be better utilized.

The best way to explain the practical applications of data mining and artificial intelligence is to meet IBM's Watson. Watson is a supercomputer that can learn. One of the most difficult things for a computer to do is to recognize natural language or human speech and be able to respond appropriately to it. It has to understand the context and the double meanings that can be confusing even for us humans. This is one of the main reasons why it was such a breakthrough when Watson, in 2011, beating the top Jeopardy winners on national TV.

In 2013, WellPoint, IBM, Watson, and Memorial Sloan-Kettering Cancer Center started working together on the first A.I. application for treatment decisions in lung cancer.

WellPoint (Anthem) has utilized the supercomputer to increase patient outcomes and reduce costs. While this may seem scary and out of a sci-fi movie (the merger of the Evil Health Insurance company with the Evil Artificial Intelligence Computer), it's actually quite the opposite. What's more, is that because of the constant improvement to Watson's knowledge base by participating doctors and nurses, *"Watson's successful diagnosis for lung cancer is 90%, compared to 50% for human doctors.*" Now let me ask you a simple question: If you or a loved one was thought to have lung cancer, who would you rather get your diagnosis from? A doctor, who would diagnosis as well as I could with the toss of a coin, or Watson, that is 90 percent accurate? Earlier, better diagnosis not only improves outcomes but saves money. Now imagine this type of technology in senior living, especially memory care, added in with sensor technology to improve medication compliance and increased feedback for medical data so that you could no in an instant how mom is doing.

To further the case for AI and Data Mining, one of the largest issues for healthcare is the immense amount of data that is being constantly updated in the world of healthcare. Healthcare professionals are expected to read, analyze and apply this information in the form of correct diagnosis and treatment for their patients. Watson, however, can not only process one million books in seconds but can also take this information and apply it to help physicians with complex patient diagnosis.

Part of the reason Watson is able to happen is infinite computing. Infinite computing used to just be for the governments. It used to be for the big corporations. You see you used to have to have enough money to build a supercomputer and then get a whole team to run it. Now, you can rent versus own. Basically, rent the supercomputer that someone else built and only use what you want or need and only pay for that very small amount. That means you can have access to faster, cheaper and more accessible computing.

Say you want to create a program or somebody out there has a great idea? Now that individual can have access to the largest fastest computer mainframes in the world and only pay for what they need. This is similar to movie stars renting a five-million-dollar necklace to wear to the Oscars and look fabulous. Things are going to just continue to go faster and faster because now anyone has access to the mainframe. The supercomputers are getting even smaller. The fastest supercomputer in the world is in China and it takes up half of a football field. There is new tech that will be released soon that will take all that computing power (half a football field) and shrink it to the size of a hot water tank for a lot less money. This change will open the doors for millions of new products to be economically developed. While it will be difficult to sort through the opportunities, imagine the time it took reading the want ads in your local newspaper and searching for your job description vs looking at Craigslist online with all the filters and being able to see 100 times the amount in exactly what you are qualified for. Tools will be developed to help you find the solutions and the providers you need.

All of this supercomputing power, data mining and sensors has allowed AI to move from science fiction to the nightly news. Meet Sophia, the world's first AI that has been given citizenship by Saudi Arabia. She's a humanoid social robot that can display 62 expressions and carry on conversations. She looks like a robot Audrey Hepburn and even seems to have a sense of humor. Hanson Robotics, along with Alphabet Inc. (Google's parent company) and Singularity Net designed the robot to be a companion for the elderly living alone or in nursing homes.

When researching Sophia, I found a weird, ok creepy coincidence. Sophia does not seem like her name was randomly drawn out of a hat. Sophia in the Gnostic tradition means the human soul....let that sink in for a moment.

## Sensors

I use Fitbits, Kardia, Nest, NuHeara IQbuds, and BioBidet toilets seats. These technologies help to keep me and my family healthy and increase independence. The Fitbits help to encourage us to move more and keep healthy. Kardia is an FDA approved EKG device (the size of a credit card) that you place your fingers on and it will help to predict 5 days prior if you are going to have a heart attack or a stroke. I recommended it to someone that was "healthy" and they did it and ended up having to have triple bypass surgery the next day which saved their life. Nest helps to regulate the temperature in the home and has cameras to ensure my grandma's safety when we are not at home. IQ buds are earbuds that help to hear in noisy situations and connect directly with the TV or phone. The best technology in this category that we have used is by far the BioBidet toilet seats. They are heated, antibacterial, wash your bum and blow dry it. It's like living at the Ritz and allows you to maintain control of your privacy as you age.

Infrastructure limits technology adoption, adaptation, and access (AAA). Infrastructure Triple-A in this sense is your worst enemy. In the early days of my career, even in Skilled Nursing, oxygen was hard-plumbed into the wall in a patient room, and so was nurse call (the device you use to call the nurse to come help you when you are in the hospital or nursing home). If you had a patient who needed oxygen, your options on a new building were to pay the excess cost of plumbing oxygen into every room to ensure flexibility, or have only certain rooms with oxygen and reject a patient if you did not have what they needed. Now, with portable oxygen machines, we don't even use it in a wall if someone needs it in a nursing home. Utilizing portable machines has allowed an estimated 2.5 million seniors in the U.S. alone, who would otherwise need senior living, to stay in their homes.

Remember the old payphones you would see around town? These have gone by the wayside due to the easy access and low cost of cell phones. Cell phones are now priced so low they can cost about the same per month as two gallons of gas for your car. With WiFi, you can even call for free internationally with Apps like Viber and WhatsApp.

The point is, technology has finally broken through the infrastructure barrier. The best way to explain this is to imagine if all of our transportation was still restricted to trains. You could only go where the tracks were, and when and where the train was stopping. Now imagine your car, and it's not just a car but it's one of those off-road cars you see on the commercials that allows you to go over boulders, through creeks and still drive on streets. The freedom is endless as to where you can go, at what time and what you want to see along the way. A whole new world is opened up for you to discover and possibly create better, faster, cheaper solutions. A mode of transportation without rails gives you complete control versus being bound by what the Train Barons set as the schedule, path and stops.

The Pro: Boomers can get off the tracks and go wherever and whenever they want.

The Con: Knowing where you want to go can be extremely confusing and overwhelming without the right roadmap or guide.

Technology and the people who use it are now free from infrastructure. From trains to cars, phones to cell phones, cable to WiFi, plumbed oxygen to O2-making machines, and hardwired electric versus batteries – it's all portable, chargeable, and wireless, which gives us the freedom to make choices.

Studies cite that 90 percent of us want to age in place in our own homes, we don't want to move into senior housing. The key is utilizing all the available infrastructure and free technology out there in order to stay in our homes longer, whining about it being confusing and thinking it's a fad. This type of thinking will only take away your freedom. My suggestion from personal experience is to select 1 or possibly 2 technologies that you find attractive and dip your toes in the water of technology. Learn what works and then, only then add more.

Progress will not be stopped: it is like a river and it will find a way to get downstream via the path of least resistance. Allow yourself to discover the possibilities with an open mind and learn what will best work for you.

Sensors are nothing new, and we don't even realize it but we already live in a world of sensors. The canary in the coal mine was a sensor, letting the miners know when it was time to get out of the mine for safety's sake. The first cars were without sensors; imagine no gas gauges or speedometers. Folks soon realized it was very helpful to know when you were going to run out of gas prior to doing so, when you needed oil, how fast you were going, and so on. I remember my first car was always on empty; it wasn't really, but the gas gauge was broken. I would have to calculate what I thought was my gas mileage constantly, and I was scared to drive on the highway for fear I had miscalculated, and I would be stuck. A gas gauge is such a basic thing, yet so valuable. Basic sensors are used on our hot water tanks, heating and air-conditioning units in the form of a thermostat, and temperature controls for the oven. Some sensors are for convenience, others for safety, and some to save energy. Safety sensors alert you to a fire, break-in or a tornado coming; energy sensors may turn off the lights after no movement for a period of time. Sensors are part of our everyday life in one form or another.

One of the simplest, most cost-effective sensor technologies on the market rarely gets discussed and most people in the US don't have them. I bet if I gave you hints, it would not even cross your mind. I first discovered this technology in Japan 14 years ago. While visiting a public restroom I was astonished to experience a heated toilet seat that had a nightlight, was a bidet and blow dryer, and was antimicrobial and antibacterial. This was a public restroom! In the U.S. I am happy to see a toilet seat and toilet paper. While this story may seem crude to you, it should not: toileting as you age is a major concern. As soon as I got back home I ordered a Japanese-style bidet toilet seat with all the bells and whistles for my master bath.

A weird phenomenon started to happen at my home...no matter how many available bathrooms there were in my house, my children's friends, our family, and even guests would find themselves drawn like a magnet to my bathroom. At first, I thought it had to be my incredible taste ☺ or maybe the heated floor, but on further investigation, it was discovered to be the toilet seat!

When we moved to a larger house to be able to have my parents and grandmother moved in with us, my only requirement was that we would have these bidet toilet seats on every toilet so that I could have some privacy in my master bath. I have to admit I was also performing my home experiment. I have been pitching these seats to clients for 11 years with no luck and wanted to see firsthand how my parents and grandmother with early-stage Alzheimer's would respond. I could not imagine having a technology available to my family to ensure their dignity and independence and not use it.

The results are in: my 92-year-old grandmother did not know what it was until it was explained to her, but now she loves it and also uses it as a shower for her bottom, as she puts it, "in between showers." My parents, at 78 and 80, think it's the greatest thing since sliced bread and feel the need to tell all the family and their friends about it.

Who knew for less than $400 per toilet I could make everyone so happy, increase their independence and dignity, and increase the chances of me not having to assist in toileting in my own home? It's a real win-win. They require no infrastructure and fit on top of an existing toilet. You simply hook the water up and then attach the electric (which your bathroom should already have). The seat tends to be higher than a normal toilet seat, which is perfect as you age, and with the nightlight, it's easier to find the bathroom at night and increases the chances of a better hit ratio if your male.

As a note, there are many different manufacturers and styles of these toilet seats. I have tried five different ones. Most allow you to control the seat and water temperature and then the intensity of the water, direction and the intensity of the blow dryer. My recommendation would be to get the toilet seat that allows the controls to be mounted on the wall so that they don't accidentally get used to steady a resident. One final note is that they are pressure-sensitive, meaning they will not spray unless someone is sitting on the seat to avoid someone pushing the controls and water spraying everywhere. These have been tried and tested in other countries and have stood the test of public restrooms – I think it's high time we give them a shot in our own homes.

Recently, we were all introduced to sensors integrated with the home environment through our smartphones. Users can integrate with Nest to turn the heat up or down before they get home, lock doors and even view who was at their door right on their phone or iPad. You could get a notification that your kids are home from school and they locked the house back up and are safe and sound. The technology centers on peace of mind and has proven to have been what consumers were looking for.

In Chapter 10, we will dive into smart homes, but it's appropriate to talk about this now with our discussion on sensors.

Lowe's Home Improvement smart home monitoring system (a sensor device) named Iris has taken this a step further by integrating a system that can be used with any smartphone and has a low monthly fee. Iris has kits that are divided into Safe and Secure, Comfort and Control, and the Smart Kit. Care, which is an add-on to the system, is specifically for the senior in your home. The system will allow for you to set rules and let you know if Mom has not been in the refrigerator in the past 24 hours (or whatever time span you choose), which may indicate she's not doing well. Cameras can be used inside the home and operated remotely. A notification can be sent to you if the front door opens in the middle of the night.

The system is intended to provide greater independence and dignity, but also keep the children from worrying when everything is fine through the sensors and knowing when the four-hour drive is necessary. Freedom and Confidence for the whole family.

While we will go into this in much more detail on smart homes, with other technologies such as Ring, security devices, connected locks and much more. The technology would not be possible without AI, data mining and sensors. While this may all seem complicated, don't worry. As I always say, you don't have to know how to fix a car to drive one. Just be open to what technology will give you the most freedom and confidence and then try it out. What's the worst that could happen?

# 6. IOT (Internet of Things) & Crowdsourcing

**IOT "What's this?"** I hear this question a lot. And if I said, "It's a global description of everything that's going on," would you wonder if I lost my mind, or worry that you're about to? Sorry, but it is that big.

Think of it as everything that's "smart." Meaning: your phones, your tablets, your GPS, your TVs, and of course...your computers. And all of these smart things are making your physical environments "smart."

Even your refrigerator, for instance, is becoming smarter and smarter. If you're not able to program it when you're reading this now, you might be able to in your very near future. Think of it like your fuel gauge on your car. When you get a smart refrigerator, it will know when you're low on eggs, milk and any other number of things. And then, beyond that, it'll order those things for you and it will set up your delivery time, too.

Technology is seeping into everything we do, and into the fabric of all our lives. I mean that very literally; the fabric of our clothes, our shoes, and our security.

While clothing that conceals cords and holds your smart devices has become popular, we will see in the next couple of years that our clothing will become a diagnostic computer of our health data, taking our heart rate, temperature, perspiration, EKG, sugar levels, O2, sleep patterns and more predicting when we may be getting sick in enough time to take supplements so that we don't get sick. Can you just imagine your Victoria Secrets bra becoming your personal health doctor and coach? Or your Hanes underwear letting you know that blood pressure has been climbing the last three days and you need to see a doctor? I know this sounds funny but underwear is worn by most people daily and you have less of them than you do your outer clothes so it makes perfect sense to integrate health devices right there by your underwire.

**Crowdsourcing** is a fancy name for getting someone else to help you, for a small price. It may be using Uber to get a ride to the doctor or pharmacy, finding someone to help clean or cook or take care of the yard or pay the bills.

There are so many different options available now from the likes of Task Rabbit, Fiverr, Uber, Lyft and even good old fashioned Craigslist. You can employ these folks safely and increase your freedom all the while paying for only what you need.

What's the difference between a taxi and a crowdsourced vehicle, besides the smell of every passenger who has sat in that back seat over the last three days? The taxi is run by a company with employees, crowdsourced cars are folks using their own car and a smartphone to pick up extra money. The real difference is in this example is that the Uber driver can rate you low if you're a jerk and if you get too many of these low ratings you will no longer be able to take advantage of working with the crowd. I actually have a friend of mine that has been banned. You also rate the Uber driver so if he was rude you can let them know and if they get too many bad ratings they will no longer be able to drive. Another feature is that all the payments are done through the app so no whipping out your credit card and having the taxi tell you he only accepts cash. The last item of attraction and why I have switched to a no taxi policy is that I can see the Uber drive on my phone, what he looks like, where his car is and can track him along the way and call or text him if needed. There is comfort and confidence that he is on his way, even if he's taking a bit longer because I can see on the app that he is just stuck at the light.

Lyft has also developed a program for seniors that need more help getting in and out of the car and also waiting for them at doctors appointments, a pretty neat solution the crowd has provided with zero employees as driver and zero cars....

Crowdsourcing seems like a new concept but it's really quite an old one. Before technology, when it was time to harvest the crops or build a barn, family, friends, neighbors would join forces to help each other out and get large amounts of work completed that would otherwise be impossible. These "crowds" would come together for the greater good or crops would go bad, or help would not come when you needed your barn raised.

Now, with harvest machines and other technologies, we are no longer dependent upon our family, friends, and neighbors to bring in the harvest or raise our barns, but we have new problems, more work than we can handle and micro-expertise that is required to build and create. The solution to these new problems comes in the form of crowdsourcing. With access that has now been created through the Internet we instantly can hire "minions" or micro-experts from anywhere in the world for a fraction of the cost previously available. Angie's List is a great example of crowdsourcing. You can hire folks for tasks and their work is reviewed by the "buyer" so that you know if they do what they say they will do. Not only do you have access to a "crowd" of potential minions, but you become a part of the crowd by providing feedback on the services you bought.

Airbnb is another great example of crowdsourcing. Basically, you can rent your home or a room in your home on a website called Airbnb. I have rented homes in Cinque Terra, Rome, Croatia, NYC, Toronto, Barcelona, Scottsdale and more. I find them wonderful and less expensive than a hotel and in real neighborhoods. It's probably not the thing you want to do if your attending a conference and need to have direct access, but if you want to get to know a city, it's the way to go. The rating system works similar to Uber, so don't trash the place or you won't be able to rent again. I can typically cut my costs in a city by half using Airbnb.

Now that we understand the basic of crowdsourcing, let's get into the specifics and review different types, how you access it and give you some examples. Crowdsourcing takes advantage of connecting specific experts or interested parties to solve challenges in either a competitive or collaborative format.

Crowdsourcing has become huge in the fields of task-related work and specialty creative work such as graphic design, video, social media, writing and coding. Companies such as Fiverr, Task Rabbit, Upwork, 99 Designs, Crowdspring, Waze, Lego Ideas and CrowdMed are just a few and have been growing exponentially year after year.

Personally, I use these companies on a daily basis and save approximately 90 percent on costs I would normally spend if we had not crowdsourced. Don't get me wrong – crowdsourcing requires your effort and engagement, but once you get the hang of it, it's like having a clone. For example, I used to spend anywhere from $2,500 to $4,000 for a logo to be developed. I would get two or three versions, and these would be in that particular graphic artist's style. If the artist was not getting what I was trying to accomplish in look or feel I would be out the money and have to research and find another designer and then start the process all over again and spend another $2,500 to $4,000.

When I had a client that was starting a new senior living company, we used Crowdspring to create a contest to develop a name for their company and ensure that it was not being used by others. The contest cost $239 and gave us 434 entries to choose from! Then we launched a contest to develop the logo for that same company through 99Designs for $499. We received 283 entries (different designs). Compare this to two or three versions from one graphic artist and you start to see my point. I had 93 different designers competing for the $499! How it works is you describe in detail what you are looking for and then designers, without being paid, send you their designs, you give feedback and then select a final round of the top entries. All the way through the designs are getting better and better based upon your feedback and sometimes a design will be "watching" vs. participating and jump in close to the end with an awesome design, similar to how you bid at an auction.

It's very much like the show *The Voice*. At the end, you select the winner and they transfer the logo and all of its rights over to you. One of the largest benefits that I have found, besides the costs, in using this format is that so often what I had in my head as the right direction did not end up being the winner. By seeing so many different options it helps you to really understand what you like and don't like with little risk. The book cover for **BOOM** was crowdsourced and then I ran a Facebook contest to see which cover of the 12 finalists everyone liked the best and I did it all for under 500 dollars!

Another example is transcription; we will have a conference call meeting with a client and for $5 on Fiverr it can be transcribed and ready to be put into meeting minutes. I don't know about you, but my team can't transcribe, and it costs us a lot more than $5 to type up the audio from a half-hour meeting. My last personal example for you is that using Fiverr, for $5 I was able to have my website analyzed and I found out I had tons of broken links that we were unaware of.

You may wonder how this is all possible. Well, some people do it to get their foot in the door with you, and for others it's a way to make income after their day job. For others, it is their actual income. While US$5 will hardly buy you lunch at a fast-food restaurant, US$5 is the daily wage for some countries and $499 for one contest equates to their typical monthly wage. One of the best ways to see if you could utilize crowdsourcing is to have your team list out all their activities in detail and then see which ones you could outsource through crowdsourcing.

One of the basic crowdsourcing platforms is called TaskRabbit. It's basically a handyman on steroids. You sign up then create a task, let's say bring the Christmas decorations down from the attic. It will then give you profiles of people that can do the task, their ratings and references and if they are available and their hourly rate. Then you choose one. It's as easy as that. I just hired someone to clean up all my garden beds from the winter. It was a huge relief as I have been traveling and could not seem to get to it. Their network is so large that IKEA the furniture company just purchased them as they noticed that seniors liked their furniture but hated putting it together. Now IKEA has a network of Task Rabbits all over the world that will do it for you and they don't have to deal with it and the best part they get more sales.

Uber, Airbnb, TaskRabbit are typically cheaper than hiring a company as these individuals have no overhead, 401K, insurance, HR manager, etc. They are barebones on the corporate side and you and I get to take advantage of it.

Essentially, there are three formats that prevail.

1. Creative Competitions
2. Bid for Task
3. Reward-Based

**Creative Competitions** work great for when you need a logo developed, website designed, an article written, or software developed. These systems work by signing up to a provider and basically placing a want ad for the work you need completed with as much detail as possible. You can either choose a site where you select how much you are willing to pay guaranteed, and then the creator submits their work and competes for the winning bid, or you allow creators to bid on the work and then you choose the creator that best matches your price point and has the background or portfolio you like the best. The key is feedback: creators need constant feedback to improve, which is easy to do through the secure portal of the crowdsourcing company you have selected.

The upside is that instead of going with your local marketing company and getting the same designer with the same ideas, you could have 60 different designers from all over the world providing you with fresh and sometimes off-base designs. You're able to shorten the design process substantially and reduce your cost. Most crowd creators (77 percent) have a primary job so this is to make extra money, to be creative or just build a reputation.

Utilizing these services can improve your look to the community and keep your events fresh and exciting at a low cost.

On a larger scale, The XPRIZE, created by Peter Diamandis, showed the world that competition creates solutions that were otherwise thought impossible. With NASA downsizing its program and retiring the shuttle, Peter decided to launch a competition similar to the one that Charles Lindbergh and the *Spirit of St. Louis* won by making the first solo non-stop flight from New York to Paris. This contest changed how the world viewed air travel forevermore. Peter created a contest to get a vehicle into space for $100K with three people and that could replicate the trip in two weeks to prove durability for $10 million. Teams from all over the world entered the contest. Twenty-six teams entered and spent over $100 million! Private space travel was born for a fraction of the investment and time that NASA could have done it for.

While Peter has created many other XPRIZE contests, the one to watch for in WellCare living is the Qualcomm Tricorder XPRIZE. The Qualcomm Tricorder XPRIZE will soon be awarded and its main goal is to put minor health diagnosis in the hands of the consumer at a higher accuracy rate than that of the current medical profession. Once this takes place, senior living will have to run to catch up to the level of quality and speed in regards to how fast the general public will be able to self-diagnose.

**Bid for Task** works differently than any of the creative competitions we just discussed. Basically, it can be anything from hiring a handyman, to organizing your bills, to ensuring quality assurance programs.

You can even make money doing bid for task, Let's say a company wants to "shop" their competition and see what someone who is not an expert would find, in multiple cities, without hiring a large secret shopper company that would entail a large contract and travel and reimbursable expenses. They could hire you as one of the secret shoppers on a task site and create a template for exactly what you needed to do, where and how you were to report back to the company.

There is one company that will pay you to send inventory data back to them via your camera phone in stores you already shop in. Let's say you're a customer of a national drug store chain, and on your visit, you notice they are out of your favorite lipstick; you pull up their app and snap a photo of the shelf. You then notice that the cough drops are in the wrong location and you snap a photo and upload it to their app. Kids are earning $80 a week directly deposited into their accounts for simply being aware in places they already visit and providing valuable asset management data in real time to the store.

Or say to have an engraving done, custom cookie cutters made, a phone answering machine message recorded by Elmer Fudd or James Earl Jones, etc. There are millions of people that have used task crowdsourcing to do these "gigs." Easyshift and Field Agent are great sites for this type of work.

**Reward-Based Crowdsourcing** can be more altruistic and/or collaborative, but in nature, it's about the work, not a monetary reward.

You could be collaborating with the crowd to identify a DNA sequencing to help find a cure for cancer, or contributing to open-source code development for new software. This category sometimes gets mixed in with gamification and data mining, which we will discuss in greater detail in those chapters. The point is that if you have a problem and want to solve it, don't try to do it by yourself or just with your team; rather, allow others to work with you.

An example of reward-based crowdsourcing is Cellvation (gamified crowdsourcing), a project that was completed in 24 hours to see the possibilities of what kind of impact a reward-based crowdsourcing app could have. Cellvation states that 428 million hours are spent playing online games each day. Their idea was to play a game and save lives in the process. Cellvation decided to figure out how to use gamification and crowdsourcing to solve malaria and cancer. Every day there are 600,000 cases of malaria. It takes 30 minutes for a clinician to look at a slide. That's 300,000 man-hours spent every day just on diagnosing malaria. Malaria is easily resolved if it's able to be diagnosed properly and quickly. To further complicate the issue, most of the cases are in Africa, where there are not as many clinicians as in developed nations.

The solution: play a game where you identify malaria. With 22 amateur people looking at the slide, they can get 99 percent accuracy and these people are just having fun playing the game. After one minute of training, they can go down to 13 people and get a 99 percent accuracy rate.

It's the same thing with cancer. Pre Screening of cancer is said to help prevent the deaths of somewhere between 3 to 35 percent of Americans. Even if they can get prescreened, there's just not enough time or clinicians to do the prescreening.

Imagine if we could potentially avoid between 3 to 35 percent of cancer fatalities through prescreening, just by playing a game. There's no money involved, but there are rewards (gaming rewards) and fun and the knowledge that you are doing something good.

Almost everyone I know has lost someone to cancer....609,640 people are estimated to have died of cancer in the U.S. in 2018. Three percent equates to 18,289 lives that could have been saved on the low side and 213,374 lives on the high side! How awesome would this be? Not to mention, the savings in medical costs to the families and system.

Foldit, on the other hand, is not a test but a real game that is helping to save lives. Drugs get tested on computer simulations of human proteins (amino acids) and in a lot of cases the limitations of computers to fold these proteins makes this a better task for humans (score one for the humans!). Per Foldit's website, protein structure is the key. "Protein structure prediction: As described above, knowing the structure of a protein is key to understanding how it works and to targeting it with drugs. A small protein can consist of 100 amino acids, while some human proteins can be huge (1000 amino acids). The number of different ways even a small protein can fold is astronomical because there are so many degrees of freedom. Figuring out which of the many, many possible structures is the best one is regarded as one of the hardest problems in biology today and current methods take a lot of money and time, even for computers. Foldit attempts to predict the structure of a protein by taking advantage of humans' puzzle-solving intuitions and having people play competitively to fold the best proteins."

The concept of dealing with disease and drug creation is very similar to a war strategy. The more you have intel on the enemy, know where they are, how many troops they have and what type of flexibility, weapons and weaknesses they may have, the better chance you have of winning the war. Folding proteins helps scientists better understand how proteins function and they can then design strategies or drugs to combat them if they have gone to the dark side and now cause disease.

Per Foldit's site, they explain the relevance to not only

cancer but also Alzheimer's, which most of us are all too familiar with:

- **Cancer:** Cancer is very different from HIV in that it's usually our own proteins to blame, instead of proteins from an outside invader. Cancer arises from the uncontrolled growth of cells in some part of our bodies, such as the lung, breast, or skin. Ordinarily, there are systems of proteins that limit cell growth, but they may be damaged by things like UV rays from the sun or chemicals from cigarette smoke. But other proteins, like **p53 tumor suppressor**, normally recognize the damage and stop the cell from becoming cancerous – unless they too are damaged. In fact, damage to the gene for p53 occurs in about half of human cancers (together with damage to various other genes).
- **Alzheimer's:** In some ways, Alzheimer's is the disease most directly caused by proteins. A protein called **amyloid-beta precursor protein** is a normal part of healthy, functioning nerve cells in the brain. But to do its job, it gets cut into two pieces, leaving behind a little scrap from the middle – amyloid-beta peptide. Many copies of this peptide (short protein segment) can come together to form clumps of protein in the brain. Although many things about Alzheimer's are still not understood, it is thought that these clumps of protein are a major part of the

disease.

Why does this matter to you? Most of the major breakthroughs in medicine have come from crowd collaboration of researchers, sharing their breakthroughs and then playing one idea off of the other to create a better solution. Now that the Internet no longer limits researchers to geographic barriers, the rate of collaboration has gone up exponentially.

To close out this chapter I would like to provide you with some examples of Crowdsourcing that can help you age with Freedom. Pick one or two and start experimenting with them. Worse case, you don't use them again. Best case, you just made your life easier and better.

- **Angie's List** – Listing somewhat like the Better Business Bureau but with real feedback from customers instantly. You can hire anything from a roofer to an electrician.
- **TaskRabbit** – Micro tasks that you need to be completed locally, could be trim the hedges or clean out the basement. You sign up through the app, list your task and they will match you up with a provider and then you choose the best one that fits your schedule, budget and meets your rating. You pay through the app so none of that awkward "where's my money." You can also rate them similar to Angie's List.

## Creative

- **99Designs –** Graphic artists from around the world at your disposal for a fraction of the cost. Let's say you want a logo made up for your family reunion, done! Or you want to have unique Christmas cards made, done! They use a contest method so you will get hundreds of entries for your agreed to a price and you just pick the one you like the best.
- **Fiverr –** This crowdsourcing app is a ton of fun! You can hire someone to do about anything (legal) for $5 and up. Leave a video message for someone in a famous voice, done! I made my Audiobook through Fiverr and have also had handwritten thank you cards made. This is a very way creative to find unique crowdsourcing opportunities.

## Chauffeur Services

- **Uber –** Like a taxi but there is no "company" you log into an app and tell them where you want to go and they match you with a driver. You pay through the app and rate each other. They just partnered with Grandpad.
- **Lyft –** Same concept as Uber. Also partnered with Grandpad. GrandPad is the smartest, simplest and safest way to connect seniors with their loved ones so they never miss another memory.

- **Vitalitix** – They call it crowd-caring," the platform provides three-way communication between "social angels" (seniors, caregivers, and community). It also connects volunteers from other networks.
- **Honor Mobile app** – An app that helps you stay in touch, informed, and in control of your loved one's care.
- **Airbnb** – Homes and rooms in homes rented all over the world at rates much less than a hotel. There are typically no services, it's more like staying at a condo on the beach (you have to clean up and make your own bed) but the experience of staying in incredible spots that are less commercial is wonderful. Like Uber and Lyft, you rate the renter and they rate you. This helps the renters to improve and keeps jerks from trashing a home.

**Home Delivery Services for Food** – Dominos Pizza, Donato's, and other fast food restaurants have been bringing food to our doors for years. However, utilizing the crowd and leveraging the Uber and Lyft drivers you can now order food on various platforms (apps, websites, etc.) and have a variety of food delivered to your door.

- **Grubhub** – App where you can order food from various restaurants and they will use Uber or Lyft drivers to deliver it to you. All money is exchanged through the app. Think meals on wheels but you can have anything you want from the best restaurants and all you have to do is order and pay.

- **Doordash** – Similar to Grubhub but it may have different restaurants.
- **UberEats** – Ubers food delivery app.
- **Cafe Courier** – Similar to Grubhub and Doordash.
- **Skipthedishes** – Similar to Grubhub and Doordash.
- **Bitesquad** – Similar to Grubhub and Doordash.
- **ClusterTruck** – When you have a family, office or friends that want to order food but pay individually ClusterTruck allows you to "link the group" and then everyone goes into the website or app and orders what they want and they pay individually all through the platform so no, gathering up of money and Bob realizes he doesn't have enough money (who invited Bob anyway?) or the issue of dealing with 5 different credit cards and getting it all right before your delivered food is cold. It's a brilliant concept and we use it all the time at work.
- **Seamless** – Similar to Grubhub and Doordash.
- **Postmates** – Similar to Grubhub and Doordash.
- **Delivery.com** – Similar to Grubhub and Doordash.
- **EAT24** – Similar to Grubhub and Doordash.
- **Foodler** – Similar to Grubhub and Doordash.
- **Orderup** – Similar to Grubhub and Doordash.
- **Munchery** – Locally sourced food that is then

prepared by chefs and can be ordered when you're ready to eat or in advance.

- **Caviar** – Similar to Grubhub and Doordash.

**Meal Prep Food** – Another new category that has popped up that seems new but is just a reboot of Swanson's, are the companies that are providing food packages that have all the food prep completed and all the ingredients included and you just have to cook them. You save time not going to the grocery store and get high-quality recipes and fresh food.

- **HelloFresh** – not cooked
- **Blue Apron** – not cooked
- **Vital Choice** – not cooked, Seafood, organic fare & supplements from wild fisheries & farms
- **Plated** – not cooked

**Aging Care Help that may not be crowdsourcing but they are worth a mention:**

- **Molly Maid** – you're probably already aware of this, you can outsource your cleaning. Molly Maid provides the talent and you provide the money and the dirt.
- **Home Care Assistance** –The only home care solution offering a balanced approach to longevity, emphasizing health, engagement, and purpose. They

also just partnered with GrandPad.

**Other Homecare help:**

- **Senior At Home Care**
- **Senior Helpers**
- **Visiting Angels**
- **Right at Home**
- **Comfort Keepers**
- **House Call Dentists –** Providing individualized dental care how, when and where you choose.
- **Silver Bills –** They take over the burden of paying bills

# 7. 3D Printing and On Demand Manufacturing

Did you know that 3D printing has been around for quite some time? You may have seen it and not even noticed it. In 1999 (almost 20 years ago), Align Technology changed the world of orthodontics with Invisalign and the technology of 3D printing. This opened up an entire market of adults who wanted braces but were embarrassed of the look. The clear orthodontic trays are manufactured by using 3D printed models representing the desired position your teeth will move. After a 3D scan is made of the wearer's teeth, a computer simulation creates a series of clear orthodontic appliances (retainers) to move the teeth over time.

While you may have been aware that Invisalign clear braces are custom manufactured using 3D printing, you'll be shocked to know companies are now printing organs, human tissue, leather, food, hearing aids, dentures, Barbie clothing, cars, drum kits, candy, and metal.

One of the most interesting aspects of 3D printing is that it is now possible to print multiple materials together. This allows for less assembly and faster printing.

Nano printing is also possible. The width of a human hair would be considered large in terms of Nano.

Nano printing is making it possible to not only make computers smaller and smaller, but the detail and microscopic scale allow scientists to nano print lattices that can grow living cells. What if organ transplant was a thing of the past and you could just grow what you needed from your own DNA with no fear of your body rejecting it. Bad burns or the need for skin could be grown and then patched in like a scene from Frankenstein except it would be all you and no one would ever know.

Another enormous implication is prototyping. It used to be that in order to take an idea to reality you would have to design it and hope it was perfect and then have a mold created or a die cast. This could cost tens of thousands of dollars. If you needed to tweak it, you would have to wait until you made your money on the first production run and then make another mold.

As you can see, this kept a lot of great inventions from talented inventors from being able to compete with the big boys because the startup costs were large and risky. This was similar to computing power that we discussed in the previous chapter.

Now, you can have an idea, create a computer model for

it and print it out, and then tweak it hundreds of times before you have ever reached the cost of making a mold.

Dentures can also be 3D printed. I am sure this will be hard to imagine but humor me. Your Dad loses his dentures and instead of having to go to the dentist and go through the entire process again, the dentist had previously given you a flash drive or uploaded the "prescription file" to the cloud and all you have to do is print the new set!

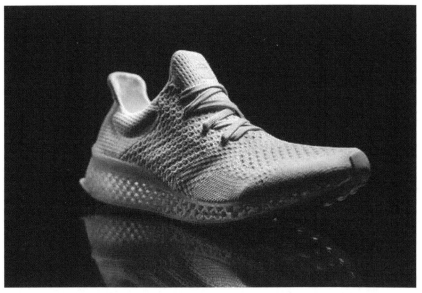

*Adidas is a trademark of the Adidas Group used with permission.*

Adidas (shown above) has 3D printed athletic shoes, and so do Nike and Reebok. Reebok and Under Armour are hitting the ground running in combining sensors, or what they are terming "wearables," with 3D printing. Some companies are printing shoes and shipping them to you after you custom-design them on a site, while others like United Nude are printing them right in the store.

Why is this relevant to Baby Boomers? Custom, Custom, Custom. Imagine going to a store where you are custom fitted for all your wearable tech, earbuds, hearing enhancers, perfect fit orthotics for your knees or feet issues, glasses, etc. all produced while you whisk away to the nearest Starbucks for your double espresso latte.

For example, our ears continue to grow, and this leads to one of the major complaints about hearing enhancement devices, they are just not comfortable. This discomfort is usually due to our ears changing and yet we are wearing a device that was fitted to us 2 years prior. Imagine being a teenager and wearing the same clothes for several years during your growth spurt. I imagine Jethro from the TV show *Beverly Hillbillies* and his pants For that matter imagine wearing the same size shoe you did when you were 6. Up until now, due to the cost and the rigid materials needed to last 10 years in the production of hearing aids, you would need to spend four thousand dollars every two years to get your hearing aides custom fitted so they would be comfortable due to the changes in your ears.

What do 3D printing, Michelin Star chefs and Baby Boomers have in common?

As we age, swallowing can be more difficult (dysphagia)

especially for those with Alzheimer's and dementia. What's even more challenging is that the harder it is to swallow; the more pills it seems we need to take. While taking your pills with apple juice will help them go down easier than water, it still can be a huge issue.

From my own personal experience, when I first started working in senior living I was shocked to see that when a resident had difficulty swallowing, the standard method of operation was to take what the meal was for the day and throw it into a blender and then let the resident drink their hamburger. To me, it was much worse than baby food, as baby food usually sticks to veggies and fruits. From a dignity standpoint, it seemed like we could be doing much better.

My family also has issues swallowing and I found this out when my grandmother moved in with me. I started having an issue and went to the doctor and apparently, your throat can narrow as you age. My grandmother and some of her sisters even had theirs stretched, sounds pleasant and something to look forward too. I had no idea how common this was, but as with most things, when your personally affected you notice more and you also try to find solutions. Really this is the purpose of the book, how can my personal desire to change how I age and those I love, help others. It's just that simple.

When I asked, what do 3D printing, Michelin Star chefs

and Baby Boomers living have in common, you may not have thought food. Molecular gastronomy and the Foodie culture have merged these all together and allowed us to be creative in our cooking, reduce risks, increase independence and have food prepared in a way that you only get in a 5 Star Michelin restaurant all in our own home. GE's 2025 Home of the Future positions the 3D food printer as being in everyone's kitchens just as we have microwaves.

There are a couple of 3D food-printing companies in Europe making a huge impact bringing this technology to our homes with a focus on aging in place.

Biozoon out of Germany is not only focused on creating foods that look good, taste great but are easy to swallow. They have lines that create molecular gastronomy and fancy cocktails. Molecular gastronomy is basically "food science"; it's a modern form of cooking that you would see at a very fancy restaurant or on a TV show like *Iron Chef*. If you're still unfamiliar with what I am referring to, it's things like oakmoss vapor, liquid pea sphere, transparent ravioli, etc. This innovative cuisine has birthed new appliances to merge 3D printing and food into everyday cooking. It's really not that amazing when you think about it. If you have ever watched the Discovery Channel TV show *How It's Made*, you have seen all kinds of food being 3D printed, from Cheetos to the beloved Easter Peeps.

This technology is now just becoming available to our homes.

The ability to deconstruct food and then reconstruct it has been mastered with these machines, allowing chefs to reimagine what food should look and feel like.

It's not all Europeans that are on the cutting edge of 3D printed food. When I met Randi Zuckerberg (Mark Zuckerberg of Facebook), she had just started test kitchens to help kids get involved in technology. Its called Sue's Kitchen. It's basically a mashup of technology and food to teach kids and their family's that tech is more than just staring at a screen. It can be interactive, and fun. They can 3D print deserts or code with candy, not sure what that is but I am sure the kids get it. It's also not in NYC or LA as you might expect, it's in Chattanooga, Tennessee. When a Zuckerberg gets involved in a technology, I think it's safe to say it's here to stay and will only get bigger and better.

Another company out of Spain called Natural Machines has a 3D food printing machine called the Foodini that they want to be in everyone's home. They have created Foodini to be able to handle high-volume restaurants (professional kitchens) as well as a single user. The machine is still a bit pricey (around 4000 dollars) but aims to be as popular as the microwave in the future.

On my first book, I was able to interview Lynette Kucsma, the CMO and co-founder of Natural Machines. The following is our conversation, and it should answer the majority of your questions regarding this new technology and how 3D food printing will be applicable.

Lynette explained how it all works "Basically the way Foodini works, is there's room for up to five food capsules to put in the machine at one time. The size of the machine is about the same as a larger microwave. You can put in whatever food you want, whatever combination to accommodate for taste or for medical needs. It's all very fresh food. The texture of the food doesn't have to be all baby food formats if you will. I'll use an example of a tomato sauce. It can't be too watery, but it cannot be overly chunky because then it's going to clog up the system and it won't print. But you could have pieces of basil or seasoning at that spine.

When I asked her if it has entertainment value or fun to

use, it reminded me of how much fun I had when I was little with my Easy Bake Oven.

Lynette responded "Both. Let's say you want to print a spinach quiche in the shape of Batman. You can find a Batman logo from the Internet, pull it down and it makes the shape. I have two kids. I have a four-year-old and a six-year-old, and it's one of my ways to engage them in cooking because they know it's kind of like playing a game at the end where you are choosing your shapes and printing and then you have different shapes. And as you know, we use our eyes as much as our mouth in enjoying food."

As you can see, 3D printing for dentures, hearing aids, clothing, prototypes, crafts and now food will revolutionize how everything is made. We are entering another industrial revolution, but it will be where we can print whatever we want, whenever we want. If you wear glasses, imagine printing out new frames and popping in your lenses if you want a new look or you just broke the frames. Bill Gates imagined that every home would have a computer 40 years ago, and most of us would have said he was nuts. Then imagine a printer in your home. Remember when there were stores that developed photos? Now you either upload them to the cloud to be printed, or print them yourself at home.

Everything is changing exponentially. They say if you

want to see if a technology will be adopted quickly into the mass market, look at your kids and teens. If it were not for teens, cell phones would have taken much longer to hit critical mass. Right now, little girls are printing their own clothing and accessories for their Barbie dolls with their 3D printers. You can find files to download for free or purchase on many sites such as Pinterest. This image of the Barbie outfits sells for $30 and that's just for a file to download. Your little girl will still need the 3D printer and printing plastic. Think of a Shrinky Dink or Easy Bake Oven on steroids.

Below are some 3D printers to look into:

- LulBot Mini
- XYZprinting da Vinci Mini
- New Matter MOD-t
- Sindoh 3DWOX DP200 3D Printer
- FlashForge Finder
- Robo 3D R1 +Plus
- Zeus All-In-One 3D
- MOD-t 3D
- MakerBot Replicator
- Ultimaker 3
- Formalab Form 2
- Routine 3-D printing

These printers range anywhere from $199.00 to thousands. Think of them like your desk jet printer you have in your house, the real cost is in the printing fiber, just like ink. Some use different types of materials to print with and some have better-prebuilt files you can download and modify and have fun with.

Why does this matter to you? 45 percent of Boomers consider themselves entrepreneurs. Not just the traditional entrepreneur that does business consulting or owns the local pizza shop. Creating and crafting can improve your quality of life by connection, increased mind work and learning new things.

Your imagination is now 3D, and unlike sculpting, you don't have to be a great artist, you can crowdsource that. Imagine you have a great idea for a new and improved gardening or cooking tool you would like to have but no one sells anything close to what you want.

You can sketch it up, crowdsource a person to build it in CAD (computer-aided design – it's what I use in interior design) for under 25 dollars, then tweak it and upload the file to have it printed for five bucks! Delivered to your doorstep is your new prototyped tool, ready for you to test and tweak and if it's a hit with the neighbors and family you might just be the next millionaire on Shark Tank or the Home Shopping Network.

# 8. Robots, Exoskeletons and Drones

**Robots**

Technically, Alexa is a robot, but the robots I am referring to here are more the physical kind of robot. We have 2 in our home, but we could have more. Right now, you can have your grass cut, pool cleaned, floors swept and have a companion pet, easily in your home with little tech knowledge. These are very "plug and pay" which basically means they are as simple as a vacuum cleaner or microwave to operate. You plug them in and then you "play", meaning you let them do their thing.

We use one of our robots "the Dolphin" to clean the pool and as a result we have cut our pool service bills by

75%. Plus the Dolphin always shows up on time, never complains, does not have the "plumbers crack" (the pool boy never looks the way he does in the movies) and does a fantastic job.

We also use a companion cat and dog to keep my grandmother who is 96 with dementia, company when we are not in the room. I was a bit skeptical on companion pets them at first, but she loves them and chats up a storm with the cat and dog. It's amazing that robots can provide, comfort, connection, and safety for very little cost.

Robots range from everything from a Roomba vacuum, introduced in 2002, that can vacuum your floors to those we see in manufacturing that have taken beer manufacturing facilities from hundreds of employees down to 10. Robotics is just another technology that depends on a multitude of other technologies. Robotics utilizes data mining and artificial intelligence, sensors and infinite computing.

Whenever robots are brought up ultimately the discussion begins about the issue of unemployment when the robots take over all of our jobs. While it is true that robots are automating factories and taking on more mundane household tasks, people will need to retrain into more creative jobs that require human touch or complex problem-solving. Let's be honest, do you miss having to grow all your own food and kill your meat? These processes have become "automated" first by other humans, then factories and now robots. While most people today could not grow their own food, this was not the case in the 1940s. There will always be purposeful work needing to be done it just may look different. The great news is the tasks most of us dislike, like vacuuming the floor, cleaning the dishes, etc will be taken over by robots leaving us more time to be creative and spend with those we love.

Per Wikipedia: "In 2012, the growth of robotic lawn mower sales was 15 times that of the traditional styles.[3] With the emergence of smartphones, some robotic mowers have integrated features within custom apps to adjust settings or scheduled mowing times and frequency, as well as manually control the mower with a digital joystick."

Jibo is touted as the "world's first family robot" which is a table-top robot that can be your phone, talk to you, help you find items on the Internet and remind you of your schedule, take family photos, act as a companion as it recognizes you and greets you, can read you a story or the newspaper, etc.

Siri from iPhone has lessened our apprehension of talking to non-live beings to the point that we are comfortable with them materializing into an actual thing that we coexist within our homes and work.

In order for you to understand how far these technologies have been developed, I am going to take you to a place that may seem far fetched, but I can assure you it's real. Just as at the 1939 World's Fair in New York they had to show fairgoers a TV with a clear screen in the back so that folks could see the inner workings of the TV because they felt they were being tricked; I am going to pull back the curtain and show you what the world has been working on the last several decades. It is my hope that you will recognize robots are here to stay and will be integrated into our lives in the very near future, and here to help us vs. the ones from the sci-fi movies that we've seen where they come to kill us!

Darpa is the government's research and development (R&D) arm that helps to further along technologies that have real-world applications in the U.S. military. The robots that I will be discussing through Darpa are public knowledge and the implications are far-reaching. They basically host contests that are very specific to what they want to accomplish, and several companies will develop technologies to try to win the contract (did you hear the see the word "contests"?). That's correct: they use crowdsourcing to accomplish what would either take too long to develop on their own or would be too expensive, through contests similar to the XPRIZE that we discussed in a previous chapter.

While I am sure they have many top-secret technologies and contests, the ones that are public are incredible. A few these awesome inventions follow. (I highly recommend you watch the YouTube videos on these; the links are provided in the resource section of the book.)

- Handle – is a 2 legged robot with wheels as feet that can do backflips.
- Spot Mini – he kind of looks like a dog and a sock puppet merged. He can empty the dishwasher, open doors, go up and down steps and it being researched as a robot that could replace your servants at home.....ok you are probably like me and don't have servants, but the point is they Spot Mini could help get all the chores done at home and save you time, much like the vacuum cleaner did almost 100 years ago.
- Cheetah – is a 4 legged robot that can run 29 miles per hour. Just fun to look up on Youtube.
- BigDog – Boston Dynamics (Purchased by Google in 2013) is a robot pack mule.
- Petman and the later version Atlas – Humanoid Robot that can perform search and rescue.
- Sandflea – think of the remote-controlled cars you give as a kids present, now attach a camera and have it jump 30 feet straight up into the air.

- RHex – similar to SandFlea, Rhex is a six-legged remote-controlled device the size of a toy car that is used to gain intel safely. Some of these technologies are being used to be in home security guards for when your home or away, monitoring to make sure that no one breaks in and all is well.

These are just fun and real examples of robot technology that will open your up to where we are headed. Do I think I will have a Spot Mini in my home soon? not likely, but in ten years it's a definite possibility that as I age robots will be serving me.

These robots are created to save lives by accessing hostage situations, gaining intelligence, conducting search and rescue, and performing mission-critical operations. While anyone could argue that the government could create an army of robots to use against us, we also understand that the term Robot = mechanical or virtual artificial **agent** per Wikipedia and basically means that we are utilizing technology to perform tasks that are simple, repetitive, dangerous or require immense strength.

Imagine that your son or daughter (who is serving in the military) is able to deploy a robot that is operated by them from the safety of a base in the United States. They are able to perform a military action instead of being in "theatre," as it is called, when you are in the warzone. This is the intention of the technology: to keep our servicemen and women safe while they are protecting our freedom.

Manufacturing has been using robotics for decades. Now, it is utilizing not only robots but also exoskeletons to reduce the impact on the human body when a process still requires the intelligence or nuance of a human to perform the task at the highest level. China is engaging in the use of exoskeletons for aging workers as you can imagine, as you age what was once easy is now harder and harder for the body forcing some to retire earlier than they want to safety issues. Now factories will be able to maintain their more seasoned, experienced employees by utilizing an exoskeleton to allow them to continue to do their job like they did when they were in their 20's.

Think of technology as the character Alfred (Batman's manservant) and you are Bruce Wayne aka Batman. Alfred was a loyal servant who tended to Bruce's every need. He woke Bruce up, reminded him of the important things he had to do, and generally kept him on track in a busy double life. Alfred was always in the background, often unnoticed, but anticipating Bruce's needs and ready to serve him whenever he was needed.

Technology should follow Alfred's lead. It should work for you so seamlessly that you barely notice that it's there unless you need it. It should help you with day-to-day life obligations and provide connection and safety. It should save you time by doing things better and faster than you would on your own and give you the best opportunity to be your best you! Whether you are jumping across rooftops as a crime-fighting vigilante, or just need more time to work on your passions, love and care for others and yourself, or just take your medications.

Technology should make your life easier with minimal effort on your part. We all live multiple lives whether it's a split between being a parent, a friend, an employee or an entrepreneur, etc., incorporating technology into our lives can help us achieve our brightest goals.

Things change and improve, but there will always be work to do. Maybe not the same work, but someone has to design the robots, maintain them and program them. Workers will have to up their skills to become masters of this new technology (machinery). A tailor would no more go back to hand-sewing a suit any more than an architect would go back to hand-drafting his design documents for your building. The benefits of technology are far too great to not to embrace them.

One of the most exciting developments in robotic technology for factories is the flexibility of programming. Imagine that robotics currently is like the first-generation computers, where you had to code what you wanted it to do just to create a simple contact list of all of your business associates (if you're under 40, this analogy will be lost on you). Now with the recent advances, you can literally teach your robotic friend via placing his hand where you want it to go and the series of actions you would like him to do step by step, and then hit save and voilà! The robot Baxter is programmed and then will fill in the blanks.

This has huge implications as we bring robots into our homes, we will now easily be able to program our robots by having them watch how we do it first. For instance, I was taught to fold towels in a German fold, three layers. They look great and take up less space than when you fold them in two layers. It's all in the details if I have my home assistance robot folding my towels I want them done my way. Not what some scientific geek at Darpa thought was a good idea.

Another example would be my grandmother who is now passed (the Italian one, Adelina or "Della" who my daughter is named after) made her ravioli. I watched her make them numerous times and even asked her to teach me which she did.... kind of. I wrote down the recipe, I watched her several times, she even had me participate. But you have to understand, she was a machine. She could make hundreds of ravioli in minutes; she would have the dough made and the meat center made and then roll out her dough on the kitchen countertop with a broom handle/stick. Then in seconds, she would literally have hundreds of meat plops in the exact size in the exact spacing, then she would lay another layer of dough on and then cut and fork each of them perfectly, again in seconds. It all happened so quickly you could not even catch the details. She was my robot.... but what if I could have had a real robot watch her before she passed and learn how she did it. We would still have her ravioli today. It's sad but with college and working I never have the time to REALLY learn how to make them and now they are lost.

Per Moley "The Moley Robotic Kitchen is a world-first: a fully integrated automated kitchen, designed for regular homes, that cooks with the skill and flair of a human chef." This robot is everything you think the future will be, it definitely stands up to the hype. The inventor of this kitchen robot believes it's a quality of life issue. 'How can I have any delicious food at home that I want at any time? That's how I've invented the Moley robotic kitchen,' says Mark Oleynik.

The Moley kitchen should hit the mass market by 2021 and cost in the range of $35,000.00, as an interior designer, this is an incredible price for what the robot does.

Not only is it performance cooking (watching the videos are mesmerizing) but it also can keep my grandmother's ravioli recipe alive. It uses two are arms and sits behind glass looking very much like a short order cook. But it can produce way more than dinner food.

I am planning on having one installed in the Limitless Living Airbnb style aging place showroom and center that I am currently building and can't wait for everyone to be able to try this new technology. I can almost smell her sauce cooking for hours on the stove, the fresh pasta, and pizza. Eating fresh vs. pre-packaged and the incredible benefit to everyone's health.

For a small amount of money in the scheme of kitchen appliances, I can bring a little of my grandmother back and let generations to come experience the same exact flavors I did growing up attending those monumental Sunday dinners with all the family. As promised, I am going to get to the really far-out sci-fi robots that are, well ... let's put it nicely: creepy. My intent is to expose you to where all this is headed so that you will understand that robots are here to stay and getting more lifelike all the time. The next ten years will be a wild ride. Think about it this way, do you remember when your phone was attached to the wall, you had to change the channel on your TV by getting off the couch and there were no seatbelts? I can...at those points in time if someone told me about today's technology I would have thought it outrageous, ridiculous and unnecessary but now I can't live without all of these things and would not go back to the old ways unless forced. Being able to adopt new technologies in mind is half the battle. Below are some examples that will seem just as outrageous, ridiculous and unnecessary.

Japan and Denmark have 2 of the top scientists in the world developing Geminoids. What are Geminoids? Essentially, they are a duplicate copy of a human in robotic form but not a clone. The premise is that the Geminoid can interact for you even if you are not able to be in the actual space. They are a teleoperated robot of an actual person. Similar to the Beam where your Skype type image is able to move around on wheels, a Geminoid actually looks like the person and speaks. If you have ever been to Disney and witnessed Abraham Lincoln speaking and moving through the magic of Audio-Animatronics technology, it's essentially the same thing but on steroids.

Japan and Denmark have entered into collaboration and recently hosted in Denmark the JST CREST / Patient@home SOSU Future Lab Workshop on portable androids and its applications in March of 2015.

**Per the website** "JST **CREST** (Core Research of Evolutional Science & Technology) research project "Studies on Cellphone-type Teleoperated Androids Transmitting Human Presence" is going to finish its five-year research on teleoperated androids. The aim of this study is to develop cellphone-type teleoperated androids that enable us to transmit our presence, anywhere and anytime. A user transmits his/her presence to a remote place and the partner in distant location can talk to him/her while feeling as if they are facing each other."

Demarks Patient@home project is testing these robots for use in their healthcare.

You might be thinking, ok now you're scaring me....What is a Telenoid, Geminoid or Elfoid?

A Telenoid is a gender-neutral, age-neutral robot that is about the size of a 3-month-old baby. The arms and legs are truncated looking like those dolls that were made of cloth before they sewed the plastic arms and legs on. They almost look alien. They transmit your presence, so if your child had one and you were traveling you could light it up and they would know you were thinking of them.

A Geminoid is a robot that looks like a person (your clone, but they are a robot) and you could activate them to interact with others for instance at work or home. They are full scale and have incredible strength. They have AI so they can carry on conversations and move around on their own. Erica is the latest version and can carry on a 10-minute conversation.

An Elfoid is a miniature Telenoid that's about eight inches high. It contains a cell phone and has a camera that captures your emotions and then transmits them to the other Elfoid. You basically hold it in front of you. I would advise only using this with someone you really care about or it may capture and project you rolling your eyes...

Of special interest during the conference was a session on seniors. The description of the session is as follows "**Portable androids for aged citizens –** The study on the portable androids explores their applications in field experiments in which people interact with one another by their (the portable androids) mediation. With the focus on the social aspects of androids that may facilitate human communications, the Telenoid has been applied to dementia care."

A session was even dedicated to Dementia – "Humanoid robots in dementia-care: Investigating if Telenoid alleviates symptoms of dementia" What I see is that when family is not near, could we use Telenoid to let them know we still think about them and love them and therefore stay engaged more. As of this writing, the jury is still out on the benefits of telenoids and dementia.

Hiroshi Ishiguro from Japan has developed not only a Geminoid that looks just like him but has also developed a female copy of a woman.

Henrik Scharfe from Denmark has also produced a Geminoid that looks just like him and states that he has become attached to having him around. His Geminoid project made him one of *Time* magazine's 100 most influential people in 2012.

It gets even creepier as they have found a way to get a microchip to merge with DNA and function as one, learning and mimicking. It's rumored that someone is looking to take his DNA and merge it with his Geminoid to create a robot clone of himself. Does anyone else think this was a plot in a recent movie? Others are working nonstop to have artificial intelligence (A.I.) in a Geminoid form and have successfully developed an A.I. that can think and have conversations. Phillip – is an AI robot that can build a model of who he is talking to with facial and speech recognition and learns every day. He seems to have a sense of humor which is one of the most difficult things for an AI to accomplish. While the YouTube video is interesting it's also unnerving. Experts remind us that AI is all around us, just think of your spam filter. While we can understand simple AI and Abraham Lincoln at Disney it's hard to make the leap to having a copy of yourself in the closet waiting to be booted up to talk to your kids while you're away on business. Pop in on mom to have dinner with her in Florida when you're in NYC or have your late husband recreated so that you're not lonely.

Why, why, why would anyone want to do this, and what could be the potential benefits? As I have been told, the reasons are to help reduce pain and suffering in humanity and, get this...they specifically mention seniors as one of the target markets!

The first way they intend on using Geminoids to reduce

pain and suffering in humanity is to provide them as an alternative to a live person for sexual use. Yes, I am serious. They hope to alleviate sex trafficking. The thought is that they could substantially reduce the need for trafficking if these Geminoids were available without legal implications. If they could save even a handful of kids, I am all for it.

Now on to a less controversial use of Geminoids. Say your husband dies after 50 years of marriage. You miss him greatly and also miss how he would help you around the house. You could order up a version of your husband (could be younger or the same age as you) and he would be your companion, help you carry out your daily routine and have the strength of Superman and never leave the seat up! Sounds really bizarre, right? I am not so sure; couples that have lived together for many years almost feel as though they have died when a spouse does. They are yin and yang, and when the other is gone it's as if a piece of them is missing. You can see this taking hold in countries that are more accepting of technology and robots than America, but the point is, it could be accepted. It's similar to looking at pictures, watching a movie or listening to a voice recording of a loved one that has passed. While you know they are no longer with you, the sounds and visual provide great comfort.

Don't think less of me but it's my job to put myself in a future position and run through if I would actually use the technology or not. If God forbid, my husband dies before me and I have the ability to get a Geminoid, I am thinking about getting 2......One in the form of The Rock, Dwayne Johnson with that beautiful smile and strength to help me while I age, and the other Zac Efron cause who doesn't need a gorgeous pool boy. As I think it through there is no reason not to get a third. Hugh Jackman, he would be my bodyguard and also teach me how to dance. So if you're reading this Greg (my husband) it will take three men to fill your shoes ?. Saved that one...

Geminoids have been tested in hospitals to see how patients would react to them and it seems that they are, in fact, creepy. People were uncomfortable with how lifelike they were, yet not human. It's a very similar dilemma that the computer-generated movie industry has experienced. We are completely OK with watching *Star Wars* and the creations that are imagined, as well as *Toy Story* and the characters that are not real, but as soon as we take this to a human form it becomes a little too real but still apparent it's not real, which creates the "creepy" factor.

Pepper by Softbank is a lot less creepy than some of the others. I have interacted with Pepper and always found her/him fun, pleasant and helpful. I am seeing Pepper more and more, at airports, banks, etc and Pepper helps with all those questions that you would normally ask at the information desk, hostess stand, etc. Pepper is mobile, approachable and will make it much easier for us to accept and robot helper into our homes as we age.

Now that I have set the stage and you understand how far-reaching robots have become in our world, I am going to review robotic technology that is being utilized now in homes.

**Personal Assistants**

Hector is a robot that is available in Europe. He is used in both smart homes for dementia and Alzheimer's residents and as a companion robot for those that can still be on their own but need a little help. He reminds you of your appointments, classes, when to eat and what to do. He can also Skype with other people, get your doctor and play games with you. Hector moves the environment in a very similar fashion to the Beam device and utilizes yes-like movements to engage you, similar to Jibo, another robot personal assistant. But whereas Jibo looks more like a minion from the movie Despicable Me, Hector actually has a face that is more similar to a human.

Clearly, the lines are blurring. Robots interact with you and not only respond, but have features that blur the line between human and robot. They are no longer being perceived as a computer software program but very often as a real friend. What's so fascinating to me is that when we connect with them on a deeper level, amazing things can happen. Our emotions are triggered and were brought out of our shells; we can laugh, become competitive, appreciate and enjoy our quality of life on a much deeper level. In short, we come alive.

While not all robots were created for aging in place, some are showing great promise for dementia and Alzheimer's. Milo is a robot with a child's face that is under two feet tall that has been used in therapy with great success with autistic children. Milo is now being tested with Alzheimer's and Dementia residents. Milo's benefits are not only that his cost is substantially less than Paro (a Japanese baby seal, stuffed animal robot that costs $6000) but that Milo can carry on a conversation, ask a resident to exercise with them and even tell stories. Milo does not get irritated when the same question is asked over and over again and speaks a bit slower than a person so he is easier to understand. He does have a wild hairdo but time will tell if this becomes an issue for older adults.

An even more engaging but less touchable technology is GeriJoy's dog and cat avatars. Essentially, through your tablet (iPad) or computer, the senior develops a relationship with their chosen cartoon dog or cat avatar on the screen that has a live person on the other end (women in the Philippines). Through previously loaded information such as photos likes and dislikes or needs, the avatar can carry on a real-time conversation! Because the avatar's voice is computerized the senior can chat anytime they want and feel they are connected to their dog or cat (avatar) vs. being confused by an accent or different voice. The dog or cat can show them photos, check up on them if they haven't engaged in a while, and remind them to drink water or just talk. Essentially creating companionship virtually.

From JoyforAll comes a line of companion pets that employ AI, sensors and robotics. They are similar to the Paro baby seal but they are cats and dogs and cost around $99.00. These are the robots we have in our home that my 96-year-old grandmother with dementia uses to keep the agitation down and for companionship.

While the U.S. is certainly making strides in robotics and technology for seniors, the Japanese have been obsessed with robots and this has culminated not only in the creation of the Geminoids that we discussed earlier but in Honda's Asimo.

Asimo is by far the coolest, non-creepy robot around. He can dance, climb stairs and now even run! Honda has painstakingly made Asimo's look and stature in such a way that we do not fear him. He is smaller than a human and has a similar body structure, but looks like he is in a space suit ready to land on the moon. His movements are so fluid that when he dances, you think he has to be human. He has rules built into him that make him step aside if he's crossing paths with a human. One of his most amazing feats of late is that he can run five and a half miles per hour. What's the big deal, you ask? Both of his feet have to leave the ground at the same time and then he has to rebalance and to land.

This is something that a robot could never do previously. It's amazing how many things you and I have the ability to do that we think are simple, but to a computer they are earth-shattering.

At Honda's headquarters, you can see multiple Asimos in the company cafeteria waiting on staff, taking their orders for coffee, making their coffee and bringing it back to them. and no, I haven't heard of Asimo doing latte art yet but I am sure it's coming. Asimo has facial recognition that allows him to not only greet you by name and know your favorites, but also remember who got what when he brings the orders back to the table. If you have seen the movie I, Robot, Asimo is very close to that reality.

I mentioned Pepper earlier but want to elaborate. Pepper is on a wheelbase vs. Asimo has legs and walks and can go up steps. Pepper is basically a pre-programmed information desk as long as you ask the right questions Pepper will give you the right answers. Asimo is more about being autonomous and still able to serve us.

The Japanese have unique reasons for developing their robotic technology not only for manufacturing but for senior living and aging in place. They have the largest population of centurions, with a growing population of women entering the workforce and not marrying. Traditionally, the daughter would take care of the elder. The Chinese are starting to experience the same issues as the result of the one child policy, which creates the perfect storm for not having enough young people to take care of the aged. Asian cultures have a high respect for their senior population and are scrambling to figure out how to meet their needs with these new challenges.

A simpler version of Hector that is basically Skype on wheels is The Beam. It was created to answer the call of all the companies that cut travel when the economy experienced a dip, yet still needed to interact with multiple teams and be there in person. The issue with Skype or GoToMeeting is that you are stagnant, only seeing what others want you to see and not being fully immersed in the situation to be able to add value.

A beam-like device was featured on the TV show *The Big Bang Theory* when Sheldon, the resident genius, decided it was too risky to expose himself to other humans. The wow factor of The Beam is that you can drive it and control where you are and who or what you are looking at. I currently have two, one I am using at a senior living clients project that we designed to answer questions remotely without having to take a trip down to the job site. the other I used to "beam" in when I travel and I want to meet with the team and help with design projects.

Imagine if you could sign into a beam at your mom's nursing home or senior living. You could literally be there, moving around, engaging with your loved one and the staff and not feel the guilt of being on vacation or living so far away?

Families could sign out the Beam and go for a walk with their mother, saying hi to her friends and even going to dinner or therapy with her? All while they are sitting at their laptop miles away. Gone would be the days of having to arrange a time to Skype (which is a pain for the staff and families), the staff getting mom to the Skype room and then just talking versus engaging.

Beam also has a small version for the home that you can use for you and your loved ones. The most unique factor is that you drive the Beam, you move it at your will. When this happens the lines get blurred between robot and human and people within minutes start treat the Beam as the person who is operating it. It's incredibly easy to use and can be turned off for privacy. The only issue is steps.

Beams currently cost is about $6,000 for a commercial model and are used in many businesses where travel is a cost or time issue. They have just started to ship a $1,500 model for the home.

While I know all of this information can become very daunting, the last thing I want you to be is overwhelmed. What I *do* want is for you to keep in mind: even if you only *adopt* one technology in this book, you will have a better life and live with more freedom and confidence than if you adopted none at all! It's not about how much you do, it's about choosing what will serve you best.

I have put in an outline format some of the top robots available today. I am sure by the time you read this there will be more to add to the list, but just as Dorothy was advised in the Wizard of Oz, we too have to "start at the beginning."

- **Servants**
  - **Outside**
    - **Yard**
      - Honda Miimo 3000
      - Worx Landroid
      - Husqvarna Automower 450X
      - Robomow RS630 & RX12
      - Denna L600

    - **Pool**
      - Dolphin
      - Aquabot
      - Hayward Tiger Shark
      - Polaris
      - Kreepy Krauly Prowler
      - Solar Breeze

- SmartPool 7i

- **Security**
  - IPatrol Riley – camera on wheels.
  - Aido
  - RoboteX Avatar III – infrared night vision, climb stairs.
  - Angee – non-moving, senses your presence. Motion sensors.
  - Orbii Monitoring – rolling camera ball – learns and gets smarter.

- **Budgee** helps you carry things around the house or yard

- **Inside**
  - **Vacuum Cleaner**
    - IROBOT Roomba 690 with wifi
    - Evovacs N79
    - Eventer Robins
    - Dyson 360 Eye
    - Samsun Powerbot R9350 Turbo
    - Neato Botvac Connected WiFi
    - Eufy RoboVac 11
    - LG Hom-Bot
    - Koios 13
    - Shark ION 750

- Mooka

- **Kitchen Bots** – now being deployed in the fast food industry but soon to hit our homes in the next 5 years. – Café X, Greens Goddess – 1000 salad combinations, Zume Pizza robots do all the dough, sauce and oven work. Noodle Duo – ramen making robots, Burgermeister has a robot that can make 400 hamburgers in an hour

    - Coffee makers
    - Compact Naboo
    - Moley launch 2019

- **Roboteam – Household Robot**

    - Israeli robotics company Roboteam is planning to launch 10 000 consumer robots this year. Previously focused on military robots, Roboteam wants to create a new robot that helps people around the house. "Seven years ago I went to visit my dear grandma," says Yosi Wolf, co-founder of the company. "When I saw her trying to carry a cup of tea and cookies and she was shaking.. I knew we could provide services to help elderly people." According to Wolf, the robot will be 3 feet high with an interactive 10-inch display. It will be able to navigate around objects using 40 sensors, and it even has a tray to carry items.

- **Personal Assistants**
  - Alexa – now can even remind you to take your medications
  - Google Home
  - Elli-Q
  - Hector
  - Sofihub
  - Silver Mother – The hub plugs into your router and has sensor devices that attach to doors, refrigerator, pill boxes, bed and more. Essentially it will sense moisture in a bed or if the pillbox has been opened. you can set it up to send notifications to yourself or your loved one if they forgot to take their pills or eat. It has a data management tool to help you track your loved one without cameras and check in when needed.
  - Pepper – dance, give directions, recognize emotions
  - Jibo – stationary family friendly interactive robot
  - Kuri -mobile, wifi, Bluetooth camera

and facial recognition – takes pictures

- Asus Zenbo – smart mobile, companionship, entertainment, control home devices and provides security, read stories
- Ubtech Lynx -humanoid that helps Alexa get mobile, play music, home security
- LG Hub – Alexa powered smart home assistant, facial recognition, share messages, play music
- Emotech Olly -smart hub and personal
- Robo Temi – video chat on wheels, music, android system
- Aido – family friendly play with kids and provide reminders for chores, keeps home connected
- Personal Robot by Robot Base -facial recognition, photos, wake up calls – talk to smart home devices.
- Buddy by Blue Frog Robotics mobile, music, cute face
- Beam – mobile video chat device that puts you in the same room with those you love, beampro2 can move the screen from seated to standing.
- OHMNI – mobile video chat robot similar to the beam

- Toyota's Human support robot – it's still a prototype but is designed to make independent living possible with assisting with day-to-day tasks.

- **Companion Devices** – many of the above robots are considered to be companion also.
  - Hector
  - Paro
  - Hasbro Companion Cats and dogs – Robots with AI that will be your best friend but never need to be taken out, fed and won't destroy the furniture.
  - GeriJoy – it's a mix of telemedicine and a companion device. A real person is on the other end but remotes in
  - Reminder Rosie – a reminder clock with different reminders for various times and reasons.
  - ElliQ
  - Grandpad – video calls, photos etc.
  - Claris Companion – it's a tablet, computer, digital photo frame, mobile phone, and remote monitoring system.

- **Mobility**
  - **Autonomous (self-driving) Cars,** Technically a robot. 33 states have introduced autonomous legislation and 21 States have passed legislation regarding autonomous vehicles.
    - Manufacturer of vehicles
      - Mercedes
      - Tesla
      - Uber
      - Google
      - Navya
      - Intel
      - Nissan
      - Apple
      - BMW
      - Volvo
      - Rio Tinto
      - Audi
      - GM

Autonomous vehicles (or you can just call them mobility robots or freedom devices) are probably have some of the most life changing implications as to how we age. Knowing we can get safely where we want, when we want, for as long as we want changes the game.....changes *our* game.

Imagine your normal yearly winter trip to Florida, Arizona or California for the winter. Most Boomer I know drive because they want their car. But it's tiring (which can also mean it's dangerous) and gets more difficult every year. But you want your car! And you want it when your there. Car = FREEDOM.

What if you could set the car and go. Once set, it would take care of the rest and you could enjoy the ride down. Stopping where you wanted and having your car when you arrive. This is just a small example of how the future will change your life.

If you have not had the chance to watch the Google Car video on YouTube yet, it's a must-see. Autonomous cars will be one of the largest game-changers in the U.S. in the next 15 years. What does all this mean for Baby Boomers? I know I wanted one of these autonomous vehicles for my teenager when she started driving, my dad could also use one as he now has macular degeneration and can't drive at night any longer so everything is a timing issue. I have personally witnessed the tragedy of my 19-year-old nephew's passing due to falling asleep at the wheel. Imagine with an autonomous car, texting and sight issues would be a thing of the past. I think the roads would be a lot safer and the data substantiates this.

Per Scientific America, More than 90 percent of car crashes in the U.S. are thought to involve some form of driver error. Eliminating this error would, in two years, save as many people as the country lost in all of the Vietnam War."

This is not to say that autonomous vehicles will be 100% foolproof. We have already seen accidents being reports, but some studies show that you can get up to eight times more cars on the highway safely with autonomous vehicles. Just taking into consideration insurance companies' thoughts, you can see why this is moving along so fast. And that's not to mention, as we grow as a country, the infrastructure would need to have a massive rework unless we can get more cars on the same roads safely.

The numbers just work. Vehicle-to-Vehicle Communication Systems, or V2V, will change how we all drive. According to the U.S. National Highway Traffic Safety Administration, they predict that integrating V2V will reduce annual car accidents by 80 percent, with goals for mandatory manufacturer integration starting in 2020.

Now Google knows this and has targeted seniors, people with disabilities, and those that need flexible transportation but could find better things to do with their time than drive.

When Google recorded the YouTube video, some of the

responses were priceless and worth hearing. The video starts out with a designer that is explaining to the first test riders outside of Google that they are special. Of special note is that you have two female seniors, a senior married couple, a sight-impaired senior male, and a mother with her small child.

The Google designer explains, "It was a big decision for us to go and start building our purpose-built vehicles. And really they're prototype vehicles. This was a chance for us to explore what it really means to have a self-driving vehicle. But in the small amount of time we've been working on it, we have functional prototypes and that's exciting."

Some of the folks in the video A First Drive on YouTube (see link)

https://www.youtube.com/watch?v=CqSDWoAhvLU

A few of the quotes from the video are below;

**Senior Female:** You sit, relax, you don't need to do nothing. It knows when it needs to stop, it knows when it needs to go. It actually rides better than my own car.

**Senior Male:** The human feeling of it is very well-engineered and it is very smooth. There is nothing that makes you feel the least bit threatened. It's impressive! I'm totally in love with this whole concept. Our lives are made up of lots and lots of little things, and a lot of those little things for most people have to do with getting from place to place, in order to connect and do things, and be with people, go places that they need to go and do things. And so there is a big part of my life that's missing, and there is a big part of my life that a self-driving vehicle would bring back to me.

The impact on Baby Boomers is far-reaching. Imagine staying in your home longer with a Google Car or similar autonomous vehicle, as you can get to your doctors' appointments, card club, dinner with friends and your grandchild's sporting events safely. Independence is maintained and safety for all involved is increased.

While it will take some time for other states to make it legal, we can anticipate that because California and Nevada have already legalized autonomous vehicles, Arizona would be next...29 states have enacted legislation relating to autonomous vehicles already.

Honda has been at the forefront in personal mobility technology, developing devices such as personal mobility devices using gyroscope technology. What's really neat about these transportation devices is that it's a blend between a Segway and a scooter that seniors use in the U.S. While a Segway could be used by a senior, they would have to stand the entire time; these you sit on, so they're more appropriate for seniors than the Segway. Honda also has another version that's smaller and is light enough to carry with you and just use it when you need it.

Core strength would have to be improved if Boomers want to use this device, as slouching and couch-potato posture won't cut it. So, you better get to the yoga studio now. If you have ever been on a Segway, you know they are incredibly intuitive; they are much easier to learn how to operate than a bike or a car. I anticipate that active independent living communities will be the first to adopt these devices, as well as seniors who are still living at home. Imagine mom's knees give her trouble but she would love to go to the zoo with her grandkids, on a vacation or just a walk with her friends. She feels guilty about slowing them down or the hassle of trying to find a wheelchair when they get to their destination. With mobility devices such as Hondas, all of those worries are gone. Mom can come without any worries and, if need be, fit the device in the overhead of the plane. Freedom and dignity all wrapped up in a nice little bow!

## Exoskeletons

While the merging of man and machine has entertained us for decades, one of my favorite TV shows in the '70s was called *The Six Million Dollar Man*. It programmed us to believe that man and machine would happen sooner rather than later. I can still remember hearing the sound they would play when Steve Austin (The Six Million Dollar Man)was slow-motion running! While it's taken quite a while to get to a real-life Steve Austin or his Bionic Woman counterpart, exoskeletons have arrived. Some exoskeletons are even controlled by thought!

Exoskeletons combine quite a few technologies to work, some of which are crowdsourcing, infinite computing and sensors. The important thing to remember throughout this entire book regarding technology is that it rarely stands on its own – it's interconnected and typically requires multiple technologies to be successful, so when thinking of adopting one of these technologies, it will be important to look at what other technologies are connected and how this will impact your execution strategy.

Man and machine have been merging since 1958 when the first pacemaker was implanted. Around the same time cochlear implants were developed. Now folks previously deaf can hear for the first time due this merger between man and machine.

This topic is so large that at the opening ceremonies of the World Cup Soccer Tournament in Brazil 2014, the first ball of the opening ceremonies was kicked by a paralyzed individual named Juliano Pinto. Walk Again, the group that made it all possible, is an international collaboration with over 100 scientists. What's shocking about this? The exoskeleton is mind-controlled through a helmet that reads the wearer's electrical activity and translates this "intention" into action. In addition, in order to provide feedback to the user, they have created CellulARSkin that provides feedback to the wearer so they know when their foot touches the ground. While this is groundbreaking, it is just the beginning in mobility-assistive devices.

The U.S. military has long been a developer of the exoskeleton as well as U.S. firemen and emergency services. Imagine for a moment that you are tasked with rescuing a family from a burning building several flights up. You're in excellent physical shape and have trained to deal with all the potential issues. You know that you may need to carry out this family, who may be unconscious. Now let's add equipment that you need to wear to not only be safe but be able to fight the fire: your fire suit (pants, jacket, boots, helmet) your air tank, hoses and extra air. This adds approximately 100-130 lbs. of additional weight on your body that you will have to take up the stairs, and then some of this will still have to be on you when you rescue the family coming down the stairs and out of the building via the fastest route possible.

The human skeleton was not meant to bear excessive weight on it to this degree. Muscles and ligaments are meant to take the pressure off of the skeleton so that it can move freely. "The Hulk" provides extra muscle that works by allowing all the extra weight to be transferred to the skeleton, bypassing the user and transferring it to the ground. Providing the user with Hulk-like strength, it allows the mission of saving the family to be accomplished with less stress and more power and reduces the damage on the hero's body that would normally take place under this kind of wear and tear. Imagine that a caregiver or possibly even you could have one of these exoskeletons to help lift someone after hip surgery. You become superhuman and don't hurt yourself while trying to help those you love.

Japan has had exoskeletons for rent for several years now. The intention was for the frail-bodied to be able to maintain their independence yet not be in a wheelchair. By far you will see that the Japanese have pushed harder on robotics than any other country to alleviate issues for their seniors. In comes HAL (Hybrid Assistive Limb), developed at Tsukuba University by engineering professor Yoshiyuki Sankai. The robot suit employs technology that reads your muscle impulses and delivers robotic assistance that can increase strength up to five times. The strength can be dialed up or down according to the needs of the user. HAL is now available to be rented monthly or week.

Recently, the FDA approved its first exoskeleton called The ReWalk for public use in the U.S. The implications are earth-shattering to how we age. Can you imagine aging without a cane, walker, wheelchair, or scooter? How much more engaged would you stay? Besides the obvious benefits to physical independence for a Boomer with mobility issues, can you imagine still being able to walk the dog, go on vacation with the family and grandkids and go up and down stairs easily?

Our minds and bodies were not meant to sit still all day, and when they do, our energy is drained out of us and erodes our value. Everyone wants to be valued, and stopping the downward spiral that is created by being constrained to a wheelchair allows you to engage in life, add value and be valued.

The ReWalk not only allows the user to get up from a seated position and walk and then sit back down, but it can help a user get up and down stairs!

Robert Woo is a 46-year-old who was paralyzed from the waist down when seven tons of steel fell into his construction trailer. He has been able to walk again due to ReWalk, a robotic exoskeleton. Robert Woo stated in an interview with CBS News, "I didn't think I could be useful and I wanted to die. The worst thing is, I couldn't even pull the plug."

Robert Woo put it perfectly. "To be able to stand up next to my wife and give her a hug for the first time, to be able to walk with my children to the park. These are things that we take for granted and I missed."

The cost could be the key: currently, the ReWalk costs $70,000. Until the price point hits around $20,000, one could assume it won't be a mass-market item for seniors and those suffering from strokes. But as we saw with scooters, once the reimbursement was figured out, it was not that folks did not want them, it was that they needed to be able to afford them.

Currently, falls could be eliminated with the new stabilization technology that is being employed by the Japanese Robot Asimo or with Segway's gyroscope.

While this technology is available today, it's a safe bet that it will move to the manufacturing sector first, emergency services and then acute healthcare. At this point, the bugs should be worked out and the price point low enough that it will have a major impact on aging in place in 5-10 years. Move over Steve Austin, Iron Man has arrived and is no longer a fantasy...

People with peripheral neuropathy (balance, walking and foot-health problems) in America come in around 20 million and most are older adults. WalkJoy believes they have a solution that will help those with peripheral neuropathy to walk normally. By placing a small device below the knee, it helps the person to walk better by stimulating nerves to send a signal to the brain that the person is walking. (Peripheral neuropathy reduces the feeling in your feet, which reduces the information the brain needs to walk properly.) The result: falls are reduced and the person has more confidence to walk, which not only engages them in life more, but gets them moving, which has numerous health benefits.

The data is in and its crystal clear, Boomers have no issue merging with machines to ensure they are able to maintain their freedom and lifestyle.

**Drones**

Drones have been on the news constantly, typically flying over sporting events, providing unique views that were otherwise previously impossible unless you owned a Goodyear blimp. They have filmed fireworks and live events. Farmers are using them to see their land without having to physically examine inch by inch, and the real estate industry is using them to get more up-to-date images than Google Earth can provide. They're being used for sports, crime control, firefighting, and delivering items through Amazon and even pizza by Dominos.

The impact of drones on aging is immense. One company out of San Francisco is delivering prescriptions through a drone system. Pharmacy items for $1 on top of the script? Because of this, you can stay in your home and have your medication delivered to you. You may drive, but when the weather is poor or your sick, the last thing you want to do is drive to the pharmacy for your prescription.

Robots (a drone is just a flying robot) have been around in some form or another for decades.

While robots have already replaced many manufacturing jobs, especially when the task is repetitive. Robots are intended to move us up Maslow's hierarchy of needs, allowing us to focus on quality of life instead of survival. We can also pursue more meaningful jobs that require our talents and mind.

As we age, the robots will serve us, be our companions, caregivers, mobility devices, and safety and connection tools.

# 9. Well-being, Mind, Body and Spirit

This is probably the MOST important part of the book. But...It can only benefit you, if you take action. It's a lot like a glass of water when you are thirsty, it won't do you any good unless you take action and drink it. Now, I know you are a person of action, because you bought the book and started to read it and you're all the way to Chapter 9 (unless you skipped ahead). This all gives me great hope for you and your future.

I personally have tried a lot of what I have in the book and can say from personal experience, even if you are consistently inconsistent (like me), something is better than nothing. I am in much better Health, Mind, Body and Spirit than I was ten years ago, and I am certainly not what you would call a "poster child" of good health practices. My husband on the other hand, works out 6 days a week, does his eye exercises, eats pretty healthy and works reasonable hours. He is in better health than me but the point is I am getting better, little by little. You have to measure your *own* progress not measure it by comparing where you are to others.

At the root of wellbeing, is that this is not a discussion about healthcare. I have worked in healthcare for over a quarter of a century, and most healthcare is really sick care. There is little if any preventive care for the body being encouraged and most of the time the essentials are left off the list. Eyes....who needs to see? These are non-essential to our "healthcare" insurance system. Ears....who really needs to hear? Helen Keller did just fine without both, she is world renown. Teeth....who really needs them? Eating is not a necessary part of being healthy...or is it? I know I am being very sarcastic but it's maddening. Throw in the fact that we are beings of not just body but of mind and spirit and these are not only ignored but some experts cannot even agree that they exist. This especially true when it comes to the spirit or soul or life spark, God within, whatever you want to call it.

We are talking about a REVOLUTION here! The kind where you take back control of your life and your wellbeing. You live in the greatest time of all humanity, where you can literally command (with some money as incentives) millions of people to do your bidding through crowdsourcing. Where you can live like a king, having access to technologies that allow you to think about things like.....what will I do with all my free time, watch Game of Thrones? Transport myself via beam or through virtual reality to Rome for the weekend? Have my robot chef prepare the same meal that the Queen of England is having or have my bum washed and blow dried by my robotic toilet. With all of these luxuries you need to pay attention to the most important ones which are the ones that impact your mind, body and spirit.

I will do my best to keep this simple and actionable, but they are all interconnected just like technology is. Remember to ask yourself the 3 questions when evaluating what will be useful for you out of this section.

1. How are you going to be able to live your life with freedom and confidence?

2. Will you be living your life?

3. How are you going to care for your mind, body, and spirit?

By now we know each other well enough, that you know I love a good analogy. It helps me to understand the world and make a concept relatable. When it comes to new technology I always follow the kids and what they are using. But when I think about WellCare, I follow the elite athletes and what they are using.

I have been blessed to have wonderful relationships with many professional and Olympic athletes. Most are older now and help others to be their best with what they have learned about keeping their mind body and spirit in optimum health.

This makes total sense right, but wait it gets better. Elite athletes (18-30 years old) intensely abuse their bodies, they have knee, shoulder and hip issues, they have memory issues, yet somehow, they show up every gameday looking like a modern-day gladiator. Perfectly fit, in mind body and spirit, ready for battle. How can they do this, when they virtually have the bodies of an 80-year-old?

They apply the technologies that we will discuss in this chapter to "hack" their systems to recover quicker and stay healthier longer. Most of which they do preemptively, but some is fix damage that has occurred and get them back in the game as quick as possible.

As I write this, Tiger Woods (43 years old, born in 1975) is even making a comeback after struggling for the past several years with two back surgeries and other issues. This is even more impressive due to his age, its extremely hard for and elite athletes to come back after surgery especially hard the older you get. Maybe we should listen to what is going on and understand that the game is being rewritten and written in our favor.

At the Abundance 360 conference, I get to witness what earth shattering new technologies are being created. This year it was all about longevity. The consensus was from all the experts, if you can survive the next 12 years then you can decide how you want to live. Of course there will be compromises, like hey you can live healthy for another 50 years but you have to give up sugar.....some of you might say, I'd rather die in the next 20 years and keep my Cinnabon's. It's all ok, it will be about freedom of choice, you will have the choice to be sick or not sick.

Let's go into the crazy not so far off future for a moment. These geniuses remind me of Edison, Tesla, Galileo, Da Vinci and Einstein. They are utterly obsessed with their theories and will probably prove them and change the way we see the world today.

Dave Asprey, Dr. Craig Venter, Mark Allen, Bob Hariri, Keith Leonard, Osman Kibar and Naveen Jain are the names you need to remember. I am convinced they are going to change the way we view the length of our life space and how we age. In no order of importance, I am going to run down what I have learned from these passionate, intelligent gentlemen that hopefully will provide you with a "future that is brighter than your past" to quote Dan Sullivan.

Dr. Craig Venter (one of the first people to sequence the human genome) founder of the J. Craig Venter Institute stated that we are "moving towards where medicine becomes proactive, preventive, personalized and predictive." The data he presented was that $1/3^{rd}$ of the people that make it to 50, don't make it to 75.....This is the kind of data that makes you stop in your tracks and say, but I'm over 50 and I'm not 75 so where does this put me. This risk is much higher as a male vs. female and the major reasons are cardiovascular and cancer related.

Because of this, the Human Longevity project combined with data from patient assessments, genome, AI and data mining they are finding information that is saving lives. Dr. David Karow of HLI says that "70 % of all cancers caught early can be cured".

In Alzheimer's disease, the Lancet commission states that "1/3 of the risk is due to modifiable risk factors" – meaning you can change it, if detected early enough. Check out more at www.human longevity.com

Mark Allen CEO at Elevian states that "Regenerative capacity decreases with age" He presented a study called Parabiosis by Prof. Amy Wagers where she took two mice, one old and one young and sewed their circulatory systems together (basically the blood that was from the young mouse was going into the old mouse and the blood from the old mouse was going into the young mouse), what happened was the young mouse ends up prematurely aging and the old mouse experiences regenerative properties of the blood from the young mouse. Basically, the old mouse became younger and the younger mouse got older. What they found was there was a protein called GDF11. It was different in old and young mice, just as it was in humans. When they isolated this

Protein and injected it in experiments, it repaired hearts, skeletal muscle, and gets new neurons to grow in the brain. What does this mean? GDF11 is reduced as humans age. You can inject it and after 9 days it makes an impact. They also found a degenerative factor. Currently they are working on animal studies in Coronary Artery disease, Sarcopenia (loss of muscle as a natural part of aging), Alzheimer's Disease and Type II Diabetes.

Based upon what the Human Longevity Inc. says are the killers from 50 – 75, I am interested in GDF11 and when it will be available, in a couple of years. It's almost as if you get all the benefits of being a vampire without all the negative.

Bob Hariri, discovered the concept of the placenta being the center of stem cell therapy and part of HLI. He is also part of Cellularity and the Applied Science & Performance Institute. The placental stem cells can be used to create any cell and your body will not reject it. It's also legal. A Stem cell is the repository for the complete human genome. How does this relate to aging? As we age our stem cells declines. Cellularity is looking at how to reboot our systems with these placenta stem cells back into your system as you age to "reboot" your system, with the stem cells that were stored from birth.

According to Happify.com we are the happiest at 18 and then don't get back to that happy point until 73 which increases until we are 85. What does this tell us? For me the study says that we are happiest when we are free to be us, at 18 our lives are ahead of us and we have endless possibilities. At 73 we have recently retired (if we're lucky), and we have the freedom to choose what we will do each day, who we want to be with and where we want to live. We are no longer bound by the obligations of a job, we can now pursue a *calling*. It may also be that between 50 -75 we will see 1/3 of the people we know, and love die. Death has a way of creating clarity, allowing you to see what living life to the fullest really means for you.

What is clear is that Peter Drucker was right "what gets measured, gets improved." When we have the data, we can correlate and correct. Data = Knowledge = Wisdom to Take Action.

Keith Leonard with Unity BIoTechnology has a mission to reshape human health span and longevity. The definition of Healthspan per Keith is the period of one's life during which one is healthy and free of disease."

Unity is focused on Cellular Senescent, Mitochondrial Dysfunction, Loss of Circulating Factors.

Our cells divide up to 50 times from the time we are born and then they stop dividing. This is when we start to age, they basically are dividing (living), dying or stopping (which is called senescent). As we age we have more senescent cells.

What Unity did during a study at the Mayo Clinic on senescent cells (SnCs) was they genetically removed the "die or stopping" cells, aka senescent cells, from one midlife aged mouse and kept in senescent cells (aging cells) in another genetically identical mouse from the same liter.

What they found was the mouse that had the senescent cells aged normally with all the problems of aging just like humans, but the mouse without the SnC's, while the same age, did not have any of the aging issues. This is earth shattering stuff. Basically, they are stopping the body from aging in terms of disease such as joint issues, sight issues, strength and heart. The deleted SnCs mouse lived 35% longer without disease.

Currently they are in human clinical trials for Osteoarthritic knees. Overall, they are targeting 20 diseases and should have 2 more in trials in the next year or so. Imagine with an IV or a shot every year you could remove (cure) macular degeneration, Osteoarthritis, Glaucoma, COPD and other age-related diseases. While time will tell, this could be the fountain of youth. Rejuvenating and restoring our tissue back to a state it was when we were young.

Dr. Joan Mannick from resTORbio is developing

innovative medicines that target the human biology of aging to prevent age-related diseases. She is looking at TORC1, a protein that may have implications on how we age. During her presentation she raised the question, why do steamer clams live 28 years, but ocean quahog clams live 220 years, a painted turtle that lives 11 years yet a Galapagos land turtle lives to 193 and a mouse lives 3 years yet a genetically similar naked mole rat lives to 28 years? Their research looks to unlock these secrets and apply them to extending our age and quality of life.

One thing to mention is that all this biohacking science compliments each other and they agree with the other findings. If I were a financial planner, I would be restructuring my clients plans to live much longer than anticipated.

Dr. Osman Kibar from Samumed is developing drugs to restore the health of a particular tissue.

Progenitor stem cells – their job is to repair and replenish a tissue as needed. Their particular research revolves around Wnt Pathway. What they found was that Wnt is reduced in degenerative disease. This Wnt gene is identical across all animals so it helps drug companies to know that it will work on humans.

The older we get, the Wnt Pathway goes off balance, Samumed has produced drugs to restore this balance. They currently are in human clinical trials in osteoarthritis (27 million Americans have it), degenerative disc disease, tendons, psoriasis, colon cancer, alopecia (baldness), anti-wrinkle (L'oreal is marketing) and with be in human clinical trials this year for Alzheimer's/ Dementia. Samumed has an injection that is regenerating cartilage in knees in about 6 months. They are also regrowing discs and growing tendons with a lotion. One of the most amazing results is that during the trials of tumor related cancers for terminal patients 4 out of the 5 patients tumors stopped growing with a pill. They have a lotion that regrows hair, and the anti-wrinkle cream gets rid of 90% of the wrinkles in 2 weeks. One patient in her 30's with terminal pancreatic cancer, she was 70 pounds, took their pill for a year and is now up to 110 pounds and back to her normal life. To say these results are astounding would be an understatement. Once through all the clinical trials, which will still take several years we could see cancer treatment dramatically change for the better. It gives me so much hope about the future.

The most exciting images were of Alzheimer's brains in lab animals, with a pill they were able to completely reverse the disease. When I questioned Dr. Osman if the mice still had their memories, he said they seem to retain them but until the human clinical trials start this year there would be no way to know for sure. Imagine the amount of pain that will go away in mind, body and spirit for those with these diseases and their families. While the drugs for you and me may not be available for a couple of years, have hope, help is on the way! We just have to stay alive long enough to be able to take advantage of all of this incredible science to turn back the clock. Imagine our bodies will be disease free and our minds will retain all of our knowledge and wisdom, this will be true freedom.

The goal for companies like Samumed is to not just stop the aging clock but to restore, rejuvenate and De-Age.

Naveen Jain, Founder of Viome, has a passion to put the drug companies out of business. He believes that fixing the gut will fix your health. If you meet him, he deeply stares into your eyes, sees and hears you. You would never guess he's worth billions. He's the kind of visionary that is on a mission and makes you believe that he will walk through fire to accomplish that mission. His concept is not new. Matter of fact Hippocrates who was born in 460 BCE said "Let **food** be thy medicine and medicine be thy **food**" and "all disease begins in the gut". Lucretius stated over 200 years ago "one man's food is another man's poison." Naveen will often quote Hippocrates, and one has to wonder if he's not channeling him.

Naveen explains that the body is made up of more foreign cells than human cells – we have less than 1% that is human, we are a walking, talking ecosystem. What I have learned from my meetings with Naveen is that 90% of the serotonin that is produced in your body comes from your gut and 70% of our immune system is in our gut lining. You know that burning in your gut when something goes wrong? That is your Vagus nerve transmitting messages from the brain to the gut. There is an actual physical connection.

Most diseases are due to chronic inflammation and his company is trying to help identify where you have inflammation and how to lessen that inflammation so that you can get your ecosystem back in balance, versus dis-ease, or being out of balance (out of ease). Knowledge is power and using this knowledge is wisdom.

While this may all seem a little Hippy for you, mainstream medicine is even recognizing the microbiome. The Cleveland Clinic even recently released a study linking the microbiome with breast cancer. What's a microbiome? A microbiome identifies all the living organisms in your body, including bacteria. We actually have more bacteria in our bodies than we have human cells, and balancing our microbiome is critical to healthy living. When our microbiome is out of whack, you may experience anything from an upset stomach to fatigue or even disease. While we are all similar, we are incredibly different, and we need to eat what is right for us but we also need to change it up based upon our ever changing gut. I have been working on my microbiome health for the past two years and I am healthier for doing it. I would encourage everyone to get Viome tested.

Dave Asprey is a biohacker. If you want control of your body, then biohacking is for you. What changes will you make to live the life you want. Headstrong, Dave's latest book talks about mitochondria. They make power for your body with food and light. If your over 40 then you have mitochondrial dysfunction. Mitochondria are your body's batteries when they are working properly. Dave wants you to be able to make energy in your body like a young person and is producing products, so you can.

Your circadian biology (what regulates sleep) is controlled by your mitochondria. The issue as Dave explains it, is mitochondria are very old, meaning they are part of the oldest part of us being human. Because of this they act like cavemen and operate on simply... Like a caveman, they don't think in a complex way, they only know three things: 1. Run from scary stuff 2. Eat everything so you don't starve to death 3. Procreate. while this may have served us in the past these cavemen are not serving us not, yet they control much of what you do. So, what can we do? We have to hack them, to make them do what we want vs. them making us do what they want.

Some of the fantastic products that Dave's company, Bulletproof Coffee, has created has helped me and my family greatly. He has a product called Unfair Advantage that helps your mitochondria to function better. My father was starting to forget things, we already have my grandmother with Dementia in the house and so this new development was very worrisome. He would leave to go to pick something up or pay a bill and would come back home having forgotten to do it, frustrated, embarrassed and scared. This went on for a month or so and then I encouraged him to take Unfair Advantage because of how much better my thinking was when I was taking it, it was like I was firing on all cylinders again. He took it and went back to his full memory, it was like we dodged a bullet! Here we thought he was starting with Alzheimer's and really it was mitochondrial dysfunction. He and I both notice a massive difference when we run out, typically we end up overnighting it. When you can't think straight, your less confident and you move through life with more caution.

As you can see the tide is turning, futurist Ray Kurzweil has created a theory called the Longevity Escape Velocity – The point where you are living long enough, that every year you are alive science is extending your life for more than one year. He predicts that this will take place by 2030, which sounds like a date from Star Trek but it's really right around the corner.

The relevance is that as we age and start showing symptoms of aging, it's rare that a brain scan is completed or labs taken to determine if there is another cause for the muscle loss or memory loss. It's just assumed that it's part of getting older.

What if the loss could be reversed through supplements and/or medication, TMS (Transcranial magnetic stimulation, PBMT (Photobiomodulation Therapy / light therapy), psychological testing, neurofeedback, lifestyle changes, bioidentical hormone replacement therapy, oxygen therapy, hypnotherapy, IV nutrient therapy, prolotherapy or platelet-rich plasma therapy. Not all of these therapies are for memory loss – some are for depression, anxiety, joint aches, etc.

Sound like anything you have? You have now been empowered to fight back and reclaim your vitality!

Reading this book is a great start, research what works for you in the list above and then talk to your doctor or find one that is up to speed on these biohacking technologies.

Currently, if you're in your 80s and you start to have memory loss, you're written off from really finding out what the issue is and if there's a possibility you could be "fixed" back to a higher level of cognitive function. SPECT scans that look at brain blood flow and activity patterns have been shown to change the treatment plan or diagnosis 78.9 percent of the time vs. just asking the patient for their symptoms. This translates to almost 8 out of 10 treatment plans being wrong when not using the technology that we currently have at our disposal.

Studies show that older adults have less active brains, but we are not stuck with this... Getting your brain back in shape helps you to think clearer and avoid the effects of mental aging. Dr. Amen has developed a system to get not only your brain fit, but a holistic system for diet that works with your brain type (he has a quiz) and then brain training that helps to reduce the risk of Alzheimer's disease.

The 2018 Alzheimer's Disease Facts and Figures Report states that "An estimated 5.7 million Americans of all ages have Alzheimer's disease in 2018. This includes an estimated 5.5 million people age 65 and older. One in ten people age 65 and older (10 percent) has Alzheimer's disease. About one-third of people age 85 and older (32 percent) have Alzheimer's disease. Of those with Alzheimer's disease, the vast majority (81 percent) are age 75 or older."

With these numbers developing a new strategy is critical, as the drugs thus far developed for Alzheimer's disease have made little impact.

Why does this matter? The oldest Boomers reached 72 in 2018, which creates more emphasis on why it's critical to manage our brain health, as only 30% is determined by genetic issues.

What does this all mean? You can determine to a large extent how you age. This is awesome news!

Simple programs to engage the brain, proper brain nutrition and utilizing technology to identify issues and aid in early detection will be the key to solving this epidemic.

> *"Anyone who stops learning is old, whether at twenty or eighty. Anyone who keeps learning stays young. The greatest thing in life is to keep your mind young."* –Henry Ford

While these doctors, scientists and biohackers and their companies are solving large age-related issues, you might be wondering if there are any small things that you can do now, without needles, tests or waiting for FDA approval.

There is...

- **Mind and Body Health**
  - **Vasper** is an incredible machine that actually builds muscle mass in older adults (almost impossible to do) and increases testosterone in males. It is basically a reclining bike with arm extensions. You put cuffs (similar to blood pressure cuffs) on your arms and legs that have cold liquid flowing through them and away you go. The cold tricks your muscles into thinking you have been working out for 2 hours but really you have only been working out 20 minutes. It's fast and brilliant. Several professional sports

team use the Vasper and well as the US military. When I tried it, I was amazed and what a workout it was and I thought I would not be able to walk for days. I then got off the machine and experienced the exact opposite, there was actually a burst of energy. So why doesn't everyone have one? The price. One machine is $50,000, that's right fifty thousand dollars. You're probably thinking who would pay that? I know one friend of mine that bought 3! When you think about reversing the aging clock and naturally increasing your testosterone it might not be so pricey.

- **Z-Health** While Dr. Eric Cobbs primary business is training trainers of the most elite athletes in the world, he still offers some applicable products such as the Balance Gym and the Vision Gym to the general public. He has developed a system to get top performance out of the top performers in the world, so they have an edge on their competition. Synching of the Vestibular (inner ear), Vision and Core are key to keeping us safely moving. When all 3 are in sync your body does not tense up which can cause injury. As we age and still want to be active we wonder why the weekly basketball game now that used to be no issue now sent us to the ER for shoulder surgery. If we neuro map prior to engaging in a sport, basically moving our body through a series of short exercises to make sure that our nerves are all "primed" then when we ying and we meant to yang we are less apt to get injured. A better example might be a car accident (stay with me) the driver who was drinking rarely gets hurt but the person in the car with them that was not who tensed up gets hurt badly. Loose/Connected = Less Injuries.

- **Amen Clinics** – Dr. Amen the author of Memory Rescue shows how a proper diet and blood flow and save your brain.
- **Hydrate IV Clinics** – Ever been sick or dehydrated and the doctor gave you and IV in the hospital? Now you can get a large dose of vitamins, hangover tonics and much more at these IV clinics that are popping up all over. Typically, they cost less than a visit to the doctor. When I travel, I go to make sure I don't get run down (sometimes prior and sometimes after my trip, it depends on how I feel). You can also get B12 shots and other health items such as oxygen.
- **Electronic Stimulation Units** – The first time my knees gave out the doctor prescribed one of these units for me. You hook a patch with a wire to your skin and attach it to the unit and then turn it on and it stimulates your muscle without

any potential damage to your body. Word to the wise if you turn it up too high, you will feel like one of those cartoons being electrocuted. Why would you use it? Some people are using them to tone flabby areas, but others like pro athletes are using them to keep their muscles in shape with zero stress to their body's while watching their favorite TV show. These are can be a hundred dollars or so up to fancy units that can get pretty inexpensive.

- **Apps**
  - ◦ **IMSHealth's Appscript** – Evaluates 40,000 healthcare apps
  - ◦ **ElderCheck Now**: Is an Apple app for Apple watch and iphone that allows the caregiver to check in with senior and access their GPS location.
  - ◦ **Skype** – While some people may consider Skype a useless app in a world of unlimited phone plans, it's important to remember these plans aren't universal. In fact, many seniors utilize the Lifeline program to access affordable cell service. Unfortunately, many of these plans offer limited minutes. With Skype, though, you can contact with your loved ones via WiFi connection. This means you'll save your limited minutes for when your away from home and you

really need them.

- ○ **MindMate –** Just like Skype, MindMate is available on both Apple and Android phones. Unlike Skype, however, this app has features that actually fight against memory loss and dementia. The app's creators used real scientific research to decide what to provide in their offering. This research led to the app offering exercise workouts, nutrition advice, brain games, and movies and music dating all the way back to the '40s. This means MindMate focuses on some of the most scientifically supported dementia-fighting activities out there.

- ○ **Voice Dream Reader –** While you can set your phone larger fonts and higher contrast, there's obviously a limit when it these no longer become helpful, and this is where Voice Dream Reader helps. The simple app allows a phone to read anything aloud to its user. Whether it's an eBook, PDF, webpage or a combination of other text, Voice Dream Reader ensures no one is left without their desired content.

- ○ **Android's Voice Aloud Reader–** Has similar features as the voice Dream Reader.

- • **Personal Health Diagnostics**

  - ○ **Viome –** Gut Biome Kit (stool sample) that will

help you to know what you need to be your best. Basically, it will tell you what you are in need of (vitamins, etc) and what you should avoid in foods so that you can tailor your diet to be your best you.

- **Freestyle Libre** – 14-day blood sugar patch with readings as often as you like. This data allows you to make smart choices for your body vs. following what is "most likely" the best choice. Not everyone responds the same to carbs or a soft drink. Find out what causes your sugar to spike and then modify your diet without having to eliminate something that you love than may not be hurting you.

- **23 and Me** – DNA testing that helps you make smart choices about your health. For instance, my father has macular dementia and when I tested I found out that I am prone to get it also. So now I am taking eye supplements to help lower my risk.

- **Human Longevity Clinic** – Full body work up with MRI, DNA and blood work. Data is knowledge, the more you know about your risks and what's not working, the more time you have to adjust your lifestyle and diet to improve your physical and mental health.

- **Kardia** – FDA approved EKG that is the size of a credit card and can help predict 5 days in advance if you are going to have a heart event. Kardia uses AI and data mining to create predictive analytics so that it knows "you" and when you are not ok.

- **MyndYou** – mobile platform to help maintain independence in early stage cognitive decline. Monitors cognitive, physical and behavioral patterns and sends alerts so that steps can be taken.
- **Steps&** – virtual smartphone assistant who guides and encourages physical therapy patients through home exercises. The interface, managed by the physical therapist, includes instructional videos; a motivation boost; and goal-setting, pre-scheduling, and tracking features.
- **AbiliSense** – they are developing apps that essentially act as a seeing eye dog would, these apps would be constantly listening to all the sounds around the user and then analyzing them and if needed sending them to a smart device for an alert or calling 911.
- **Mybitat** – is a smart home product that is partnered with Samsung to data mine ( take all the information it sees and hears in the home with sensors) and develop patterns for normal. When they are out of the "normal range" the system alerts pre-selected contacts.

- ◦ **Easy to Connect (E2C)** – a Basic Smartphone (available in the United States and Israel) and a Basic Tablet (available in Israel) designed to help seniors easily access the latest communication technologies with large print, one-button navigation, and other streamlined processes. A Basic Smart TV and Basic Smartwatch are coming next, per their website. While you may think this is not for you, you may be taking care of a parent or a spouse that may need this technology. Any tech that can reduce the stress of the Boomer (the primary at home caregivers in the US), is good tech to me and worth mentioning.

- **Mind Health** – Mind health is a combination of exercises for the brain, proper nutrition for the brain and learning to tune out the noise (our brains were not built to handle all of the noise of the technological age, this causes excess fatigue and stress). A major change in the last 20 years is that doctors used to believe that our brains were hardwired and could not change, but now they know we have "neuroplasticity" in other words, you CAN teach an old dog new tricks. We also now know that with the proper mitochondrial function, oxygen, blood flow and vitamins in our brain, we can make out brain better! Not just slow the aging process but get back what we thought may have been lost forever. This changes the game and puts us in the driver seat of our destiny.

- **Amen supplements** – Dr. Amen has excellent supplements to help your brain function the best. Please get some blood work done to see if you are deficient in vitamin D, Niacin, etc. then avoid sugar and start exercising.
- **Meditation** – decluttering our mind from the noise of everything going on is critical to your brain health. 10 minutes a day in the morning can do wonders. I was against meditation at first as I thought it was a religion, then I discovered Headspace. This app guides you through ways of calming your brain and reducing your worries. If you were like me and thought, I pray I don't need to mediate. Prayer is an active petition, meditation is about not thinking about anything, and instead.... clearing the mind. They are not in conflict, and meditation can help with depression and more mental clarity.
- **Brain Games** – Anything from playing cards, crossword puzzles, words with friends to apps like Luminosity will help keep your brain firing and active. I like to think of it this way, in high school I took 4 years of French, I was able to speak, understand, write and read French at a decent level. Now, I can barely say Bonjour (Hi)

or Oui (Yes). The point is if you don't use it, you lose it.

- ○ **Bullet Proof Coffee** – There are many items on this site from mold free coffee (mold is predominant in most coffees and cause inflammation) to Unfair Advantage which happens to be my personal favorite. It helps me to get rid of my brain fog by increasing my mitochondrial function. As I had mentioned, my grandmother who has dementia lives with us and so we are all very sensitive if someone else's memory seems to slip. My father was having trouble remembering and we were all so worried that he may be going doing the dementia path. He is in his late 70's and still works every day. I had him start taking unfair advantage and within a week or so the memory issues were all gone! No kidding. We were all relieved and he is now a raving fan. They have many more supplements that are excellent to keep your mind and body at its best performance levels.

- **Sleep Health** – Many experts would tell you that Americans have some of the worst sleep habits in the world and that most of us suffer from poor sleep health. This affects our body and mind health and our ability to heal. Going to bed at the same time each night is key (which I am terrible at) as well as not looking at any screen device, TV, Tablet or cell phone for at least one hour prior to bed. Doing these 2 simple things can help you sleep better and become healthier but if your like me and lack the discipline, below are some items I have found very useful.

- **Bullet Proof Mat** – This is a mat the size of a bathroom floor mat with what looks to be plastic golf spikes sewn into it. If you have trouble sleeping, try laying on this 10 minutes before you fall asleep. The premise is that most of the time you wake up (with the exception to go to the restroom) due to heat or discomfort. But if you use acupressure to get the blood flowing through the entire back prior to sleeping you will have a much better shot at staying asleep. I use mine nightly and my mother who has had 5 back surgeries was having issues again and I asked her to start using it and .....yep they went away, it was blood flow.
- **Noise** – ensure that you have a noise machine if you are a light sleeper, white noise can help greatly to give your mind something to focus on so that it does not wake up at the furnace turning on. These are easy to find online or in any store.

- **Amber light vs. Blue light** – Make sure that your night light is an amber color (orange/yellow) vs a white/blue tinted light. The blue lights will tell your brain it's time to wake up and it will be more difficult to not only get to sleep in the first place but get back to sleep once you have gone to the restroom.
- **Human Charger** – one of my top recent finds! This device looks like an iPod with earbuds but it does not play music. Scientists in Finland found through blind studies that you could introduce light into the brain not just through the eyes but through the skull. Your body's sleep cycle is controlled by your circadian rhythm and this is controlled by sunshine. We spend 90% of our time indoors and if you live in a climate like I do, where 3 months out of there year there is no sun, sleeping and even staying happy can be a struggle. The Human Charger has solved this issue by pumping sunshine (blue light) through your ears via the ear buds for 12 minutes when you wake up. It's magic! Seriously, the studies of people with SADD feeling less depressed are 70%, it helps with jet lag and dementia. For me, it just changed me from a 3-alarm girl to a 1 alarm girl and now I wake up fresh and ready to go.
- **Vielight Neuro Alpha and Gamma** – Wearable

light therapy device. · This device stimulates the neurons in the brain to repair and heal themselves, it uses photomodulation which is a form of light therapy. It Improves mental clarity, enhances the immune system, improves energy, stimulates inner systems, such as improved circulation and complements other existing wellness routines.

- **Wearable Technology**
  - **Smart Watches & Activity Trackers** – Help you to track your steps, heart rate, and other items. The idea is that when we're accountable to ourselves and others, we make better choices. There are way too many to mention and they change daily but here is a place to start. Remember, it's all about what's important to you and don't forget the look and feel. I have bought many of these devices only to stop using them because I did not like them due to size or look. If the watch is a fitness/activity tracker I have put those in a separate category.
    - **Bioguard** – Mayo Clinic device to remote monitor chronic or at risk patients & Scales/apps to update and track weight.
    - **Proof** -is a unique and elegant solution to knowing if you have had too much alcohol to drive. It's a wearable wristband that can

discreetly analyze your BAC levels through your skin.

- **Fitbit:** Fitbit uses builds on this concept to engage us to get moving within a community of other Fitbiters.

  - **Alta –** Fit almost any wrist size, basic tracking / Steps (no heart rate monitor or GPS)
  - **Zip –** Lets you track and compete with others and has a clock. Tracks distance, steps, and calories burned. No Heart Rate or GPS.
  - **Surge –** Tracks Heart Rate, GPS, Steps and has a clock.
  - **Charge 2 –** Reminds you throughout the day to move. Tracks steps, Heart Rate, GPS and has a clock.

- **Garmin Vivofit Fitness Band –** For under 100$ this wearable tracks your activity level and then assigns you daily goals. It tracks sleep, steps, and calories and can also hook up to a heart monitor.
- **Samsung Gear Fit 2 –** It's a high-tech wearable with an accelerometer, barometer, gyrometer, heart rate sensor, and GPS. You can answer calls with it and it has a touch screen.

- **Withings Go** – Simple display that switches between activity and clock. Does not have a Heart Rate or GPS.
- **Moov Now** – It has no screen and the tracker can last 6 months in between charges. Must use a smartphone to see data.
- **LETSCOM Fitness Tracker HR** – Activity Tracker Watch with Heart Rate Monitor, Waterproof Smart Fitness Band with Step Counter, Calorie Counter, Pedometer Watch for Kids Women and Men – for under 30$

- **Smart Rings**

  - **Oura** – Ring that your pulse ox levels, heart rate, respiration, body temperature, and sleep. This is one of the smallest wellness devices available.
  - **Thim** – Ring that tracks and helps you to improve your sleep. It is only a sleep ring and not meant to be worn during the day.

- **Livio Ai Hearing aid** – This is not just a hearing aid. This little, comfortable gadget is the newest wearable. It can easily monitor your body and brain health. It also translates 27 languages, has fall detection, is connected to your phone, and can even be found by GPS tracking when you can't remember where you left it!

- ◦ **Apple's AirPod** users to enable the operating system's Live Listen feature, which turns their phones into remote directional microphones. They then may place their phones closer to a speaker to better hear the person's words
- ◦ **Hearing Aid Apps** – A hearing aid app connects to your smartphone and allows you to use your hearing aid to make and receive calls and control volume.

Most of the current wearable tech is in its early stages for health management but it's great for fitness management.

As listed above, Fitbit is one of the most popular name-brand data-gathering bracelet that tracks your activities and encourages you through gamification (we will go into detail on gamification in a later chapter). They capture the hearts of fitness enthusiasts that desire to get better results through tracking and tweaking. As the old saying goes, "What gets measured, gets improved."

Basis is a fitness-and-sleep-tracker watch that was released in the past few years but claims to be the most comprehensive health watch on the market...and has now been discontinued. This is the issue with tech, you have to be flexible to change to the next thing.

I personally used this watch and loved the data but found it too large and clunky for my wrist, which meant it was hit or miss if I would wear it. Having said that, what the watch did was still outstanding and gave me a push to get more active and develop better sleeping habits. The watch not only documented when you slept but also tracked your REM and how many times you tossed and turned and woke up. It employed gamification and also tracked my heart rate, steps, calories burned, perspiration and body temperature.

I was mortified to find out that I burned almost the same amount of calories while I was sleeping as when I was awake! I guess sitting at your desk all day doesn't get the heart pumping. Just by learning this information, I have become more active about getting up and taking breaks, stretching and taking the stairs instead of the elevator. By all accounts, I look fit, but my sleep score was terrible. The device woke me up, to say the least, to the benefits of sleep hygiene. I started darkening my windows, using the TV and phone less prior to sleeping and creating a consistent bedtime, which helped my score tremendously. The important thing is I feel better.

Many experts believe that Americans' terrible sleep habits are at the center of our health issues. The data you can see below is my personal data from the watch that gets synched with my computer and the Mybasis site. For less than $200 for the watch (no monthly fee) I had more health information reported 24/7 than my grandmother had when she was in short term rehab. As we have discussed prior, it's not the event that we should all be concerned about, but how to monitor the data we can easily obtain to reduce the risk of an event or put in place an action plan prior to the crisis happening.

Hearing aids are a wearable technology that has been around since the seventeenth century, with the first electronic hearing aid in 1898. Cochlear implants became revolutionary for those with extreme hearing loss but required surgery. Now there's a hearing aid from Sonitus called Soundbite that is bone-conducted but requires no surgery and is FDA-approved. The really exciting part of this new technology is they are moving towards the ability to implant a hearing aid in a molar. Imagine a world where you're not having to look for the lost hearing aid anymore.

An assistive hearing device is the Nuheara IQbuds. They are wireless assistive hearing devices that work just like earbuds you use with your phone or tablet, matter of fact they double duty as earbuds. They have various settings to control what you are hearing. This is important as louder is not always better. The IQ buds hook directly to the TV so that others 3 rooms over don't have to hear what you are watching and best of all I can hit restaurant mode and hear what is being said at my table instead of all of the noise. While these don't replace a hearing aid they are an excellent cost effective solution pricing out at a 10$^{th}$ the cost of hearing aids.

Livio Ai Hearing aid is one of my favorite new technologies. Why would I get so excited about a hearing aid? Because it's not just a hearing aid. This little, comfortable gadget is the newest wearable. Forget the wrist to monitor your health; the ear is where it is at.

Blood vessels are much closer to the device, so it can easily monitor your body and brain health. It also translates 27 languages, has fall detection, is connected to your phone, and can even be found by GPS tracking when you can't remember where you left it! I plan on getting one and using it not because I have a diagnosed hearing loss. I do have difficulty hearing in restaurants but this is not the primary reason, I want my health monitored, but I have never been a fan of smartwatches. And, I can get rid of my Bluetooth earbuds. But the biggest win will be confidence when I travel. I will be able to understand the waiter, taxi driver and the hotel clerk.

We have discussed hearing, now it's time to move onto glasses. While Google Glass has been in the news over and over again, they have never taken off like Google thought they would. They have, however, inspired others to make glasses that are a combination between the sci-fi Oculus Rift virtual-reality gaming glasses and the glasses actor LeVar Burton wore on *Star Trek: The Next Generation* which allowed him to see even though he was born blind.

What if they could make the blind see, or at the very least, help those that are sight-impaired with degenerative eye diseases see?

Professor Kohn of the University of California has developed such a device. He is using computers and math to correct the distortions seen by those with macular degeneration. He is working on both glasses and contact lenses that would be tailored toward the individual user.

If you have an aging parent this may be of interest to you. The Japanese have been using smart diaper technologies for babies and these now have moved to the senior market. Adult smart disposable diapers are outselling baby smart diapers due to the rising age of seniors in Japan. The technology sends a wireless signal to the caregiver that lets them know if the diaper is wet. This is a tremendous advancement as it lets your elderly parents age with dignity. It's especially true if you're dealing with a parent who has dementia or Alzheimer's; they no longer need to be undressed to check to see if there is an actual need for a change.

So far the sensors that have been developed in Tokyo measure moisture so you or a caregiver can know when to change someone, but Pixie Scientific's diapers, also alert you when the sensors detect a urinary tract infection, prolonged dehydration, or developing kidney problems."

I know with my grandmother's recent issues, these would be a great help to our family at home. Quite often the onset of dementia gets misdiagnosed and it's actually a UTI (urinary tract infection). In older people, UTIs can cause confusion that mimics dementia, left untreated a UTI can cause serious health issues. Sensors of this type could not only help with the correct diagnosis and getting mom or grandma back on her feet but also increase dignity.

Another great wearable tech that we have been trialing out is the Freestyle Libre glucose monitor. My dad was recently diagnosed with sugar, as he likes to call it aka diabetes. He has high blood pressure and macular degeneration so with the sugar diabetes diagnosis it's a real concern. They each impact each other negatively when not in the normal ranges. While at a business conference I met a young man wearing a small disc arm patch about the size of a half dollar. I asked him if he was quitting smoking and I congratulated him. He said no, from all his readings, sugar controls how well we think and our health and he wanted to understand what foods and drinks impacted his sugar and then how to make changes so that he could be his best self...

A wearable device to compile data before you're sick that helps you to make wise choices, what is this world coming too! I asked him if they were expensive and to my surprise they were not, I asked him if I needed a doctor's prescription and to my amazement, you did not. So, what did I do? I immediately ordered 2 of them and had them shipped to our home.

I believe I mentioned before that I live in a social experiment where I experiment on our family on the best way to live our best future by using design ideas, health devices and anything that might be called "smart home tech". Well, this was another perfect opportunity to try another experiment. I introduced the idea to my mother and father, and they were excited. I think that in the past, we have had so much success that they now look forward to the next new tech that I bring home to make their lives better. So far, we have had pretty good success.

A little back story, my father loves bread, Arnold Palmer sweet iced tea and in general deserts. When he came to live with us he was a huge Pepsi drinker and we asked that he stop drinking pop as it was so bad for him. Out of respect for us, he did but then found Arnold Palmer sweet iced tea as a replacement. To me it was like mainlining sugar, this seemed to be our weekly battle.

Until that is, the Freestyle Libre Glucose Monitor Patch entered our lives. The idea for the patch is that if you could know immediately what made your sugar go up or down without the pain of constant daily pricking, you could then adjust your diet and exercise to how your body reacts to foods vs. what a doctor thinks it would do. This could mean that my father could keep some of his favorite foods and drinks. Or he would have factual data that the iced tea, was killing him. The thought that he could have a patch on his arm with a hair sized needle that would stay on for 14 days and then read his blood glucose levels at any time was very appealing.

As you can see, sensors are just starting to surface in everything from how we take our medicine, when to change a diaper, reading the blood glucose levels in our tears & our arm patches, knowing how long we slept, how many times we tossed and turned, and what our sleep quality was, to sensing the electrical impulses in our brain and allowing us to move body parts that are paralyzed.

Athletes and the military are at the forefront of sensor

technology but make no mistake, it is weaving into all of our everyday lives.

Soccer shoes have been equipped with sensors to discover the speed and how many miles a player runs in an average game. The results are staggering: a pro soccer player runs eight miles during a 90-minute match. Basketballs, soccer balls, and tennis racquets are now equipped with sensor technology to help you understand how to strike the ball better or how often you're hitting the sweet spot with your racquet.

Fabrics are currently being released that have sensors woven into them. Our children and grandchildren will not ever argue with the TV over whether or not the ball went into the goal and the referee made a bad call because the ball and the goal plane will both have sensors and automatically signal when a goal has happened.

A quick search on the Internet reveals new categories of wearable tech every day, and health management is looking to be the largest sector. Baby Boomers not only need to integrate home IoT (Internet of Things) and safety sensor technology but also follow health monitoring that allows with ease the monitoring of your heart rate and sleep and your loved ones. The game is certainly changing.

Anyone involved in healthcare or if your dealing with an elderly loved one, you know that medication compliance is difficult. Besides toileting issues, help with medication seems to be a huge driver to getting mom into assisted living after she forgot to take her pills or took too many, sending her to the hospital. While senior living has done a great job at managing medications, it is still unclear if they are working properly for the individual. What if we could know that mom not only took her medications but they are working? Proteus Digital Health has a solution for this which, when taken to the next level, could also be used for mom to stay in her home longer as data will be immediately sent to the doctor or caregiver via Bluetooth if she has missed her dose or taken too much.

Proteus Digital Health has created the first FDA-approved ingestible sensor (the size of a grain of sand) for medication compliance and feedback. The sensor reacts with the stomach acid and creates a type of potato battery with its small amounts of magnesium and copper. This allows data to be sent out to a smartphone or other device. The device passes out through the normal process.

Currently, Helius (Proteus Digital Health's name for the pill) is being utilized for heart failure and hypertension but looks to add other chronic disease management. This is the first step in ingestible sensors that will be coming down the pike for all of us, giving us better feedback loops. If we know what is actually working immediately, we potentially could take fewer pills, with better results.

## Induction Looping Technology

Almost 1 in 2 people over 65 have some form of hearing loss. Those with moderate hearing loss have triple the risk of cognitive decline/dementia, per AARP. Hearing can cause not only issues for the person not hearing but also for the loved ones, coworkers and friends that constantly have to repeat themselves, get misunderstood and just plain frustrated all around with the situation. When communication becomes difficult, folks become paranoid and or disconnected. Of course, we have had hearing aids for years but this only helps with part of the issue. While Induction looping technology has been around for years, it is not well known. The basic premise is that if you are hearing-impaired, even with a hearing aid it is difficult to hear in a large setting such as at church, sporting events, airports, concerts, activities, dances, etc. Basically, it's tough to hear with a hearing aid anywhere a microphone or speaker system is used. Induction looping allows those with a hearing aid to hear directly from the microphone without all the background noise. Louder does not always mean easier to understand.

How it works is a loop of wire is installed in the space that can be small or large events and uses a speaker system; this can be anywhere from a living room, to a stadium, bingo hall or church. The wire transmits a magnetic signal to a T-coil, which is found in 70 percent of all hearing aids. The hearing aid can then directly hear what is coming out of the microphone, TV or speakers without all the background noise. Europe has been using this technology for years but the U.S. has been slow to adopt. There are some 36 million people with hearing loss in the U.S. Michigan has been the largest initiator in the U.S., having installed induction looping systems in several hundred venues as well as the Detroit airport and Michigan State University's basketball stadium. New York City is adding hearing loops in almost 500 subway information booths and for all future taxis they will be equipped with lopping technology and have been branded the "Taxi of Tomorrow."

As with most great technology, the looping solution is simple and elegant. You might be thinking why can't Bluetooth solve this issue without the cost of installing a looping system? Bluetooth technology sucks battery power, while the telecoil requires zero. This gives the telecoil a major advantage. Another advantage is that looping can be utilized in both large and small areas while other wireless technologies (such as Bluetooth) can only be used in small areas. Finally, hearing aids all have different proprietary wireless technology depending on the manufacturer. The telecoil is the only universal wireless receiver.

**Key Benefits to looping system:**

- **Universal** – compatible with any manufacturers hearing aid

- **Affordable** – looping technology is a very low-cost technology per space
- **Energy Efficient** – zero drain on the battery
- **Flexible** – can be used in large and small spaces
- **Scalable** – you can start with one space and add on over time
- **Easy** – simple to operate, both for the resident and the staff, reduced listening effort
- **Independent & Convenient** – if looping technology is available the hearing-impaired person is completely independent of the need to ask for a portable assistive device and then having to plan to pick it up and remember to return it
- **Dignity** – there is no need to ask to be moved closer or get earphones to hear

Interviews that have occurred after installing the technology will bring you to tears. Those enjoying the technology speak about how they were able to enjoy the event, hear the sermon for the first time in years or just simply be part of the moment with everyone else, laughing at the joke that was told. In the *Hearing Journal*, Dr. Remensnyder tells of other denominations attending services at St. Mary's of the Annunciation Catholic Church because they have a hearing loop. We all want to engage in life and hearing is one of the most important senses that allow us to do so. Being alive means being able to communicate, something as simple as being able to hear the joke, TV show, sermon, or your favorite song connects us and feeds our soul.

Positive statements from the study were as follows: "I didn't have to work so hard to hear the speaker"; "In a loop I don't need to read the captions"; "No more need to read lips"; "**Freeing**"; Feels like I have normal hearing"; "The clarity in a loop is **amazing**"; "I could hear things my wife could not hear"; "**So much better I cried**"; "I would not attend (meetings, church services, etc.) if they did not have a loop"; "It is awesome to be able to understand, not just hear. I don't think folks with normal hearing can appreciate just how awesome it is!"

Imagine, with this one simple technology, how your life could improve or that of a loved one by the simple fact that you or they could hear what was being said. TV's could be turned down. Engagement in conversations would exponentially increase, creating more energy and a higher quality of life for all. The ripple effect will be enormous for everyone involved.

For more information to find out how you can have this technology implemented into your home, please see this link: **http://www.hearingloop.org/vendors.htm**

**Telemedicine:**

Remember back to ancient times...those days of yore when you actually had to go to the doctor for a pregnancy test? Okay, maybe you don't remember, but it used to happen. Now? You go to any drug store and buy a kit. This kind of instant testing tool has created enormous flexibility in our lives. Now imagine it in much broader terms and you've got "telemedicine."

Telemedicine is about technology giving you're the ability to take your doctor with you. You're no longer going to be anchored, or some might say, "imprisoned" to whatever your support system is...I.E. your doctor, your health records, real time real data. With Telemedicine you'll never have to make an appointment to go to the doctor again unless you want too.

Telemedicine will allow you to take your doctor with you wherever you might be, Scottsdale, Rome, a cruise and your home. Telemedicine can range from a phone call to a video chat. Insurance companies are finally starting to see the light, that most office visits could have been handled with a video call and they are paving the way to making telemedicine billable in several states. Add in any health data device such as Kardia, Freestyle Libre, iPhone health devices and the doctor can read your vitals while you're in two different places. No more having to go to a clinic when you're out of town and give a random doctor your 60-year medical history!

**Fitness:**

Let me start by defining what I think "fitness" is all

about. To me, it encompasses physical, emotional and spiritual wellbeing. I really believe that without all three you're not "fit." And technology is here for you in this part of your life, too; it's providing a lot of tools that can help you take back control your body, mind, and spirit.

There's yoga, there's the memory diet, the balance gym, and the vision gym—just to name a few. Think of these tools as helping your body (which maybe has been asleep for a little bit) wake back up.

The more you sit, the more you disconnect. And anytime you start disconnecting you start degrading, then you start atrophying in body and mind, and your spirit, too.

Maybe you're finding yourself sleeping more, maybe you're not engaging in conversation, or reading or growing in any number of ways. By making the choice to physically reconnect, you start to plug back in. And I do see this very much like physically plugging an electrical cord back into a socket that has been disconnected...it brings you back to life.

Fitness is about reconnecting your body, mind, and spirit so they can work the way they all should work, allowing you to be fully powered up. The action of plugging back in, of making the connection, is being proactive. You can start with taking a walk around the neighborhood, volunteering, reconnecting with old school mates on Facebook, going to church, temple, mosque or wherever your religious preferences take you, joining a club, start taking supplements, meditating or whatever you desire. Start with one and then add on when you feel you can. In a year from now, I promise you will be glad you did. If you thought today you had another 50 years to live guaranteed and the only thing you could do is decide if you wanted to live them sick or healthy, which would you choose and what actions would you be willing to take today to know that in 5 years you could live free from sickness, assuming that was your choice.

To me, this is all about "what lifts your spirit." For some, it's meditation, for others its movies. While some might find it in a religious community, others feel it in nature. And then there are others who use yoga to connect to their spirit, and still and others who connect through music, dance or laughter.

So, this is really all about remembering what you need to do or what you need to experience that feeds your spirit. Think of this as your new "prescription"; it's tailoring something so specific to you because you know who you want to continue being as you age.

My point is that most of us live with a mentality that the future is dimmer than our past. Both mentally and physically. With all the technology coming down the pike in the future that will help us to be our best and what you will learn in the upcoming chapters, we have to consider that we are in control of our destiny and that means we have to make wiser choices. Left to our own devices *we will* binge-watch TV, *we will* eat all the Thin Mints, potato chips, ice cream (pick your poison) and we will choose to disengage from something that we used to do and liked but it has become an effort (Well, at least I will!).

While I am far from retirement, when I do retire, I used to think of it as not having to show up anymore. What a profound statement, let it sink in, I used to think retirement meant *I'd stopped showing up for life.* I would no longer have to show up for anyone anymore, I would not have to look nice or be accountable. Then I realized that I don't want to live my days out looking like a hot mess, not adding value. So, I have decided that "retirement" for me will be choosing where I can add value. Showing up with all of me but less stress. Having the freedom and confidence to do what I want when and where I want. So when you're changing to that season of your life, the question is, *"How do you balance being a human being who's doing what you want to do, and also the one who's making wise choices for your long term health and wellbeing?"* *"What happens when you lose community?"*

Remember it's up to you, what's the "prescription" you need to write, for your life to be the best it can be.

# 10. Cannabis and Aging

Full disclosure, while in high school, I was pretty intense, I had friends in all different social groups and was even the president of the entire high school. My mother was also the high school head cook. This created 2 problems for me. First if I got busted drinking I would be kicked off of student council and second, my mom heard about every party in the lunch line. I needed to maintain my good kid status, but be able to decompress a bit. For me the answer was smoking pot. I didn't do it every day but enough that I knew what I was doing.

When I went off to college, I worked 3 jobs just to make ends meet so paying for anything recreational was out of the question and then I got married and had kids. My days of smoking pot were a high school memory. As I got older, a lot of my highly successful friends would mention they smoked.

Then the laws started getting passed in Colorado, California and others. CBD oil and the benefits for seizures and other health issues came on and even the positives of pot with cancer and dementia.

Yet my industry of senior living was still ignoring the subject even though every conference when we all got together was focused on how to attract Baby Boomers to senior living. My first thought was, heck yeah the space we design are awesome but my friends would never come unless they could have their freedom and still use marijuana or cannabis.

So I decided to break the silence and conduct an anonymous survey of Boomers and cannabis use, that I could use to start a health dialog. What I found, opened my eyes. When I presented the data online I was even challenged that it was overstated... I can tell you that this is not the case, we had over 15,000 respondents from all 50 states and eliminated 4,000 responses that felt illegitimate (possibly generated from a bot).

It's an important conversation to explore. The stigma of using cannabis is fading and now with Canada making it legal for both medicinal and recreational use, I believe we will see a huge shift in the US moving towards federal legalization.

## Cannabis for Boomers: An Emerging Market

For many baby boomers, the word "marijuana" conjures up nothing more than, perhaps, some recreational memories of the 1960s. But, a significant number of seniors have displayed increasing interest in the potential benefits of marijuana, also known as cannabis, as a modern-day option for improving their quality of life. Both medical and non-medical cannabis products hold potential benefits for this aging segment of the population.

As more states have legalized its use, there is a lot more to know about the applications of marijuana. Let's examine this phenomenon to see how legal cannabis has become big business, how marijuana might help boomers with certain conditions, and what forms of this substance has become available for purchase.

## The Need for Real Data

As a senior living designer for over 25 years, I am often shocked at how our industry talks out both sides of its mouth. My clients say they want younger healthier "residents" in their senior living homes, but do little to meet them where they are. Let's be honest, if you have ever visited someone in an assisted living, memory care neighborhood or short-term rehab (a facility for recovering from knee and hip replacement), then you know that even in senior living homes that charge anywhere from $45,000 a year after taxes up to $150,000 a year, you are getting a beautiful environment with lots of services and amenities, but you are not buying freedom.

This is the rub for boomers. My Boomer friends don't just want freedom, they consider it oxygen to their soul. Let's factor in that recreational drugs were a definer for their generation and quite a few have never stopped, at least when it comes to marijuana.

When attending functions within the Senior Living Industry, discussing the need to allow senior living residents to partake in cannabis for medical or recreational reasons is like showing up to church in your underwear. I'm not talking about a housecoat. I'm talking about full on Tyra Banks Victoria Secret undies and maybe even the wings! You're looked at like you're the antiChrist, to put it kindly.

I did not even realize how polarizing the subject was until I was on the construction site of one of our projects (a brand new senior living, which is incredible) for my client. I got onto Facebook Live with the property in the background (I did not mention it by name) and asked everyone to take my marijuana survey. By the time I left the site and my plane landed back home, I had 20 messages telling me to take the post down ASAP. The client wanted in no way to be associated with Marijuana. I apologized and immediately took the post down. But, this was exactly why I decided to do the survey: someone needed too. Everyone was running around scared to death of the marijuana monster in the closet. Yet they didn't even know how their customers felt about the subject. We need real data to start the conversation.

I felt so strongly about the need for the data that I

postponed the release of this book, which was completed in March 2018, to be able to include this chapter and the results....

## The Survey

Let's clear the air, I am not pro marijuana or against, I just wanted to have a discussion with my clients about the subject with real facts. My personal mission is to help seniors and boomers embrace living and to help move from fear to freedom, and this subject seemed to evoke a lot of fear.

The survey consisted of 12 simple questions:

1. Do you live in a state that has legalized marijuana?
2. What state do you live in?
3. If you currently use marijuana, why?
4. If you do not use any form of marijuana, why?
5. If you use marijuana, in what form?
6. How often do you partake?
7. Why do you use Marijuana?
8. In what social setting do you use Marijuana, if you do?
9. Do you grow Marijuana?
10. Do you use CBD oil?
11. If you use CBD, for what reason?
12. Your Age.

I opted to use a third-party quiz software called Leadquizzes to ensure those taking the survey their anonymity. This means, other than the answers to the questions above, I have no data, no emails, nothing.... In hindsight, I wish I would have asked if they were male or female and possibly their economic bracket which I think would have been very useful.

I posted the survey on LinkedIn, Instagram and Facebook and ran ads, posted videos and begged my coworkers, vendors, family and friends to not only take the survey but to pass it along. It took around a month to get around 15,000 takers and over 67% completed the survey which translated into over 10,000 legitimate survey results!

The results, frankly, shocked me. I believe they will create a great dialog for senior living and our nation on aging and aging in place and what it means to have the freedom to be your best you.

## The Rise of Medical and Non-Medical Cannabis

Times have changed since the U.S. universally condemned all forms of cannabis as illegal substances. In recent years, laws broadly legalizing medical use have been enacted in Arizona, Hawaii, Montana, North Dakota, Minnesota, Michigan, Illinois, Arkansas, Louisiana (except for smokable forms), Ohio, West Virginia (but only for cannabis-infused products), Pennsylvania, Maryland, Delaware, New York, Connecticut, Rhode Island, and New

Hampshire. Additionally, recreational marijuana has been legalized in Alaska, California, Oregon, Colorado, Massachusetts, Maine, Nevada, Vermont and The District of Columbia. These changes have brought a major new industry into being. It's estimated that the total CBD market will be worth some $2.1 billion by 2020.

There's nothing new about the use of cannabis. Cannabis has been administered both recreationally and as a medicine for thousands of years. The ancient Chinese used it to treat everything from gout and rheumatism to memory problems and malaria. Ancient India found it helpful for digestive issues and also brewed a relaxing tea with it. Medieval Europeans incorporated cannabis into folk medicine, and as early as the 1700s, American and English doctors were studying marijuana's potential medical benefits.

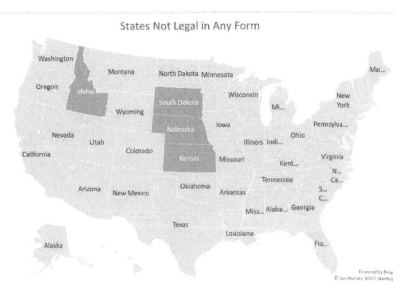

States Not Legal in Any Form

States Legal Recreationally

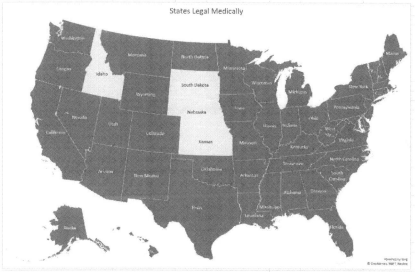

States Legal Medically

## A Variety of Benefits

Today's society has access to many different forms of cannabis, some of which produce altered states of consciousness and some of which do not. The difference is the presence or absence of THC, the compound that actually makes people high. Recreational marijuana depends on THC to create its relaxant effects. Cannabis products created for medical use focus on another ingredient instead – CBD, or cannabidiol. CBD oil and related CBD products don't have psychoactive effects. They do, however, offer many promising medical benefits, especially for seniors and boomers troubled by age-related complaints. These include:

- **Alzheimer's disease** – In the laboratory, the THC in recreational marijuana has demonstrated the ability to slow the progression of beta-amyloids, the abnormal protein accumulations associated with Alzheimer's dementia.
- **Cancer and chemotherapy symptoms** – Elevated cancer risk is a sad fact of aging. Cancer patients often experience nausea and vomiting, whether they're receiving chemotherapy or palliative care. Smoking marijuana appears to ease these symptoms, along with neurological damage related to their cancer treatment.
- **Chronic pain** – Seniors often struggle with chronic pain conditions such as arthritis. Studies indicate that CBD products can help relieve arthritis symptoms and other forms of chronic pain. The THC in recreational marijuana also appears effective for easing chronic pain symptoms.

- **Mood disorders** – Depression, anxiety, and other mood disorders can afflict empty-nesters and seniors dealing with various health problems. CBD products can help manage these potentially dangerous conditions by increasing the amount of serotonin in their system.
- **Loss of appetite** – As taste buds age and sedentary habits take over, many seniors lose interest in food, leading to malnutrition. Medical marijuana can re-activate the insula, an area of the brain that encourages appetite.
- **Glaucoma** – Pressures inside the eye can destroy the optic nerve. This condition, known as glaucoma, becomes more prevalent after age 60. Medical marijuana has demonstrated the ability to lower high eye pressure, potentially preventing blindness.

## The Many Faces of Cannabis-Based Products

Cannabis comes in a wide range of delivery methods, of which smoking marijuana is only one. While smokable marijuana is indeed available in a variety of strains and brands, CBD oil (the key ingredient in many CBD products) can also be found in:

**Tinctures** – Tinctures contain CBD oil in a fluid base. In its more highly concentrated forms, you only need to put a couple of drops under your tongue.

**Capsules** – You can take CBD capsules just as you might take any nutritional supplement.

**Topical products** – CBD creams and lotions can be applied directly to the skin. This can be an effective method for treating chronic joint pain and inflammatory disorders.

**Sprays** – CBD sprays are meant to be sprayed into the mouth or throat. While the concentration tends to be weaker than that of other delivery methods, sprays are quick and convenient for travelers.

**Vapes** – It's possible to take CBD oil in vape form. But this delivery method, like the spray method, provides relatively small dosages.

**Edibles** – There are a variety of CBD candies, gums, and other edible products on the market today (at least for residents of states in which such purchases are currently legal).

## The Results

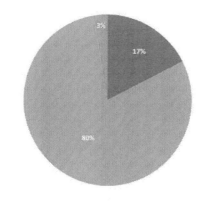

■ Borderline Boomer 50-53  ■ Boomer 54-72  ■ Silent Generation 73-93

**Who took the survey?** 80% of those that took the survey were baby boomers, with 17% being a borderline boomer, ages 50-53, and 3% over 72 years of age.

While I am very pleased to see such a large sample from the boomers, I wonder if we would have had higher results on those age 73 and up had we conducted a house to house or mail survey. I believe the channels that I dispersed the survey possibly hampered them to respond.

**Where do they live?** The biggest shocker was that 37% of the respondents live in a state where marijuana is not legal for medical or recreational use!!! This gives even more validity to the survey as this is not "it's legal here so of course, we do it" result. I have to be honest, I thought the majority of the respondents would have been in California, Colorado, and Nevada since, "everything is legal" there; however, Florida, Ohio, California, Texas, Michigan, Pennsylvania, Oklahoma, Indiana and Illinois had the top respondents in terms of number of people who participated in the survey.

### Do you live in a state that has legalized marijuana?

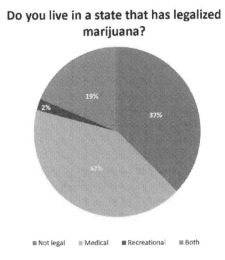

■ Not legal　■ Medical　■ Recreational　■ Both

Certain states that are technically legal for medical marijuana like Ohio may still be perceived by the general public as illegal and hence why the 37% of respondents stated they lived in a state where it was not legal.

# How often do you partake?

**How often do you partake?**

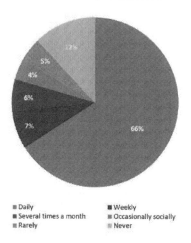

- Daily
- Several times a month
- Rarely
- Weekly
- Occasionally socially
- Never

According to the survey, 66% partake daily....if this is not enough to start a conversation then I don't know what is. 12% have never used and 5% do so rarely. This leaves 83% that partake often with the vast majority doing it as much as they brush their teeth. Keeping in mind that 80% of the folks taking the survey were boomers, these numbers could be even higher if we took out the silent generation and the Gen Xers.

## Why do you use Marijuana?

While 17% don't use at all (this ties into the 5+12=17% above), almost 50% partake both for recreational and medical reasons.

**If you currently use marijuana, why?**

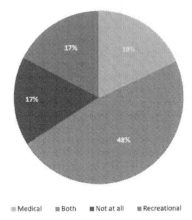

▦ Medical  ▧ Both  ■ Not at all  ■ Recreational

Then there is almost a 50/50 split for those surveyed that partake for either medical or recreationally.

# Do you grow Marijuana?

Do you grow marijuana?

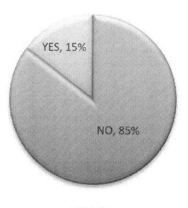

NO YES

Survey says NO......at least 85% of the respondents don't. This means in those states (41 states) where recreational marijuana is not legal, boomers are getting it somehow.

**If you Use Marijuana, do you use CBD oil? And why?**

62% of respondents use CBD oil and the vast majority, 59%, use it for aches and pains.

**If You Use Marijuana do Use CBD Oil?**

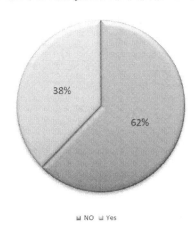

A shocking note on the results was that very few sited glaucoma for their use of CBD which may be due to the fact that they are using marijuana instead.

Other than general aches and pains the highest percentages of use were for Anxiety 11%, Arthritis 7%, Insomnia 7%, Cancer 3% and Back Pain 3% were the other top reasons for using CBD oil.

While the numbers were too small to chart, there were several respondents that were using CBD for their pets.

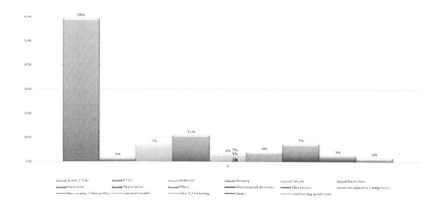

As you can see, there's a great deal more to marijuana than just getting high, especially for seniors battling health and comfort challenges. My hope is that cannabis is just like any other bio hack that gets used responsibly to improve our quality of life as we age. And if you're wondering, I don't partake at the moment, but the thought is not out of the question for the future.

# 11. Smart House

Let's start by explaining what a smart house is, the typical definition of a smart house is a house that your appliances, lighting, heating and cooling, water temperature, TV's, phones, music devices and cameras and security devices are all connected. They talk through Bluetooth or WiFi from a hub and can be accessed by your phone, you directly or your computer. They learn your patterns of life and can save you money by shutting items off when they know you don't normally use them. They can alert the police, wake you up, make your family room a disco and turn off the stove if you leave it on too long.

It all sounds fantastic, right? Sign me up right now.....Here's the glitch. Smart homes are a lot like fixing your own car, I am sure it will get simpler in the future, but they currently make me feel like I am 16 again.

On one of those days, I remember thinking "I was always pretty good at fixing my bicycle so how hard could it be fixing a couple of items on my car be?" With all of the confidence that a teenager has, I went to into one of those auto parts stores like Pep Boys or AutoZone. All I remember is how it felt like I was in a factory that built cars vs my local and very easy to use department store. All I needed was some oil and a couple of windshield wipers. When I got to the counter, I found out that even those required that I know the make and model of my car. He asked the make and model and I answered.....red (it's the same answer I give politely to the clerk when I check in to the hotel and I'm asked the same question about my rental car, thankfully they take pity on me). Apparently "red" would not do, so I went back out to the parking lot and obtained the needed info and then made my way back up to the counter with the make and model as requested. They opened up this huge blue book, found my car and what oil it took and the model number of wiper blades and then I was off to the races, or so I thought until I had to install them and add the oil. It all worked out but it made me realize that it was a bit more difficult than I anticipated.

Creating a Smart Homes is a lot like getting oil and wipers for your car, if you know the make and model and are willing to put some elbow grease in, then you can probably do it like I have on a fairly small scale. Granted it's just my Google Home hooked up to my Phillips Hue lights but I am able to turn the lights on and off, play music from my phone through Google Home, ask Google a joke, the news or the weather but she still won't sync right with my calendar. I have yet mustered the courage to try and connect the Nest thermostat and camera to the Google Home as they are working fine right now and who knows, I might screw it up and leave us without heat in the middle of winter.

Now, if you're the Iron Man type or some sort of tech genius then God love you, you probably shouldn't even be reading this chapter. This is for those of us that are just trying to figure this thing out and understand how it can improve our lives. To put it simply we want technology to serve us and not the other way around. I don't want hooking up my smart house components and keeping them all connected and functioning properly to become a full-time hobby or worse a job. I just want to live like the Jetsons did with my 3D printed food, Rosie the robot cleaning everything, flying cars and may get my figure back to what I looked like in high school, that's not too much to ask right?

Now that I have scared you, don't worry too much because chances are good you already have a smart home. Do you have a thermostat that automatically tells the furnace to come on and off based upon your settings? If you have a garage, do you have a garage door opener? Maybe one even mounted on the inside of your house? Do you have a device or contraption that alerts you when someone is at the front door (Hint: it's also called the doorbell)? I know I am being funny, but these are smart home features. Does your car connect with the garage door and open it without another remote in the car? Can you auto set your coffee pot to come on in the morning, so that hot cup of joe is waiting for you on command? Then I bet you already have a smart home.....oh my gosh I just realized I sound like Jeff Foxworthy when he does his shtick. Sorry about that I must have been channeling a redneck.

It does all make sense that it all should be able to be connected together in a plug and play model similar to our phones or our computers. When it's done right it's very similar to how your phone works. Your phone is the basis of where all the apps sit, they work together to help you take a photo, post it to Facebook or email it to a friend. You can put reminders on your phone to have it start playing music to wake you up at a certain item and so on. It's all a beautiful ballet. Now think about your phone having more apps, this time they control your thermostat, lights, TV and more.

How cool can it this be? Your driving back from visiting your mothers for the weekend, before you left you set the thermostat to 65 degrees, its 0 degrees out now and you should be home in an hour, you login to your nest app, which is on your phone and turn the temperature up to 72 degrees (I realize some of you just thought I was nuts going above 70, don't judge me, I have a low core body temperature). And Voila! When you walk in your door, it's nice and cozy as it can be.

Or let's try another scenario, you are at the airport

getting ready to take off for vacation and you realize you left the stove on.... have no fear, an app is here! Just log on and turn it off. No worries, no panicking phone calls to neighbors, friends, and family all the while trying to figure out how to get them the keys. Just use your finger and swipe and it's done. Smart home technology can provide immense peace of mind, energy savings and the conveniences that we will discuss in the many products that are on the market to help make your life more enjoyable.

If you're thinking this is a fad, it's not. Smart homes were actually created in Scotland in 1975. This "fad" is similar to indoor plumbing. Smart Home technology is already here, the problem is, I would never even think about trying to plumb my house or install a new hot water tank, yet the commercials and big box stores make us think it's as easy to install as plugging in a radio and turning the knob to our favorite station. My advice after I have struggled, is this... hire an expert just like you would hire an electrician or plumber. You'll have none of the pain, leaks or fires and all of the benefits of the technology.

One thing to know is that it all works with a strong WiFi. You need to get this installed in your home first and make sure that it's boosted to the whole house. I ended up having to purchase an Orbi system after I had purchased another system and wasted my money. The reason the first system did not work was that it took my WiFi system and split it. So the signal was degraded the more people we had on it the slower it became and depending on how far away you are from the "home" hub you could end up being in a dead spot. With the Orbi system somehow it does not split the signal but "clones" it instead (best way I can describe it). Not only are there are no dead spots and it was incredibly easy to set up. it also works with google home and Amazon Alexa (we have both) but similar to the nest I am not ready to work through getting these all connected yet.

Once you have great Wifi you can decide what is most important to you and your family. Do you want to stream Hulu, Netflix, Amazon Prime, YouTube or other to your TV? If you don't know what these are no worries, I will explain. Remember things are changing so fast that you NEVER need to feel dumb about technology. I am at conferences with the most brilliant minds in the world and when someone presents a new technology we all look at each other like they must have looked at Galileo when he first described the world was round instead of flat. Eventually, we all get it. Just remember you don't have to understand the physics behind how a car works or how to fix it, to be able to enjoy driving it.

If you're not familiar, with names I have listed above, these services they are basically like cable TV (on demand for you). Instead of waiting for a show to air, you just search for it on your TV, phone, computer or tablet and watch away. Typically these come with a monthly service fee. Sometimes Amazon Prime comes with basic movies and TV but if you want to watch a new release that still may be in the theatre you pay an extra fee on top of the monthly. The really cool thing about having a smart TV is you can get a "stick" to plug into it and that will give you access to these services that you already use on your phone or computer or tablet.

Amazon has the Firestick, Apple has Apple TV, Google has Chromecast and there is also Roku. You only need one. So, if you are an Apple user then Apple TV is probably your best bet. If you're not an Apple user (I am not), then you can pick any of the others. I went with Firestick, it was easy to install and I even got one for my mother. She stated she "felt like a queen", while I am not exactly sure what she meant by that, I know that she loves the wide range of movies and shows, etc. that she has access to through our Netflix, Hulu and Amazon accounts. It is possible to have a stick and the accounts and get rid of cable. I may try that, but I need to make sure I don't lose Oak Island first ?

What this means to you is that all of your entertainment will now be linked to all your devices. And if you have an Amazon account, you can even hook up Alexa to your TV and order items online. It's like the Home Shopping Network taken to the next level.

You may be wondering at this point what if all my stuff in my smart house that is now connected to the Wifi loses power? I highly recommend getting a generator, if you live outside the city. We have one, even though we live in the city because we live in a 4-generational household. When I moved my parents and grandmother in with us, it seemed too big of a risk not to have one and now I am even more glad we did get one. I am not sure which would be worse, then freezing to death or the Hallmark channel going out (please know I am kidding this is just a little 4 generational household humor).

We have discussed the general concepts of a smart home and many of the pros and cons, but how does it work? And further, besides being really cool how can it help me age in place?

A smart home can be set up to sensors for motion, temperature, heat, etc. and this could trigger certain actions that you want. The way this happens is by using a site called **IFTTT** (IF Then, Then That), basically you decide what you want to happen and what needs to trigger that to happen and then it will work like clockwork.

For example, I could set up a scenario that **IF** the motion sensor picks up movement from my grandma's room after midnight, I **THEN** get an alert to my phone or from Google Home. Or it could be as simple as **IF** the pizza guy is on his way from dominos and the app is linked to my smart home, it could **THEN** turn the front porch light on as he is driving down the street, helping to signal the house to him. You can also use it for things not related to your smart house, but mostly on the internet. Let's say I set a trigger that **IF** a birthday notification comes up in my Facebook feed **THEN** it would automatically respond to that person with a Happy Birthday! Now, I don't do this but I could, and so could you. This logic is pretty simple but may require an expert to help set up. Let's try one for fun, **IF** the smoke detector goes off in the kitchen, **THEN** the BLANK shuts off. I am sure you got that, it was the stove that needed to shut off. Pretty simple like I said, but pretty helpful. One more to get the hang of **IFTTT**, **IF** you are speeding on the highway, and you see a police officer, **THEN** you..... ?

While there is no way for me to go into all the details of Smart Homes, I believe that a Smart Home is not just what we spoke about above, it's also the intangible things that are "smart" in a home. I call it creating Soul Space, you know that place where your soul just feels at ease. It may be that perfect chair, or the sunshine coming in the breakfast nook in the morning. Whatever it is, when you can create it your house, your house **THEN** becomes your home. I also believe you can employ smart design strategies to help you age in place with ease in your home. I have developed The LOVE method as an easily, adoptable, design guide to improve your confidence and freedom as you age in place.

But before we discuss The Love Method in Chapter 12, I want to introduce you to some wonderful smart technology for your home, this is not a complete list and typically I do not list them alphabetical nor in order of preference.

In an effort to expose more people to technology and how it can increase your freedom and improve your quality of life, I have purchased a 1914 French Opera Style Manor House that I will be converting to a Limitless Living AirBnb Style Home.

The goal of the renovation is to create a unique and flexible space where anyone can experience the latest technologies in home living while also creating a community space for people to come together and connect, stimulating the imagination about what the future could hold as we age.

This renovation will showcase the technology we discuss in this book and be updated periodically to ensure the best limitless living tech available. I think of the space as a living showroom for aging in place technology, from furniture, fabrics, flooring, toilets, baths, sinks, lighting, WIFI, sound, maximized closets, TV, kitchen and much more. A spa will be integrated into the space with the latest aging bio hack technologies available.

This will not be a senior center; it's designed to be a true community space to bring all generations together. It will be a place for community events, meetings, and classes as well as a space that will be designed with technology intended for Boomers to be able to age in place and continue to contribute to the community.

I want the renovations to create "soul space" for everyone to enjoy and come together with "everyone engaging in the same space and feeling great about being there and able to connect on a deeper level with one another."

Boomers will find a space that showcases the possibilities of technology assisting them as they age. The technology will be integrated directly into the renovation. The best aging in place designers will partner with highly touted vendors such as Shaw Flooring, Delta, Kohler and Toto to redesign various rooms and demonstrate the reality of limitless living.

As you can see, writing this book has more than inspired me, it's created a whole new living laboratory that everyone can be a part of, moving us from fear to freedom! Now let's continue with the smart home tech.

**Comfort & Energy Savings**

Comfort is a difficult subject, everyone feels temperature differently and the actual temperature can be felt differently by the same person depending on what material it is coming from. As we age it becomes even more of an issue when we take into consideration the loss of fat in our body's (fat insulates and holds our core temperature, hence the flabby skin), blood pressure and less mobility. Depending on where you live, keeping cool could be your issue or keeping warm. Whichever the case, when we are comfortable, we are at ease.

One of my favorite smart features in our home for comfort is the radiant flooring (heated floor) for my bathroom tile floor. It may not seem like something you want to invest in but it is incredibly comfortable to visit the bathroom and touch a warm comfortable floor instead of a cold tile floor that sends shock waves up your spine. I know this because sometimes if resets and turn off, typically on a cold winter night and it seems to be reminding me of how awesome it is and not to take it for granted.

While the radiant flooring may be my favorite, the Nest thermostat has a close second in my heart. Our Master bedroom was an addition from the previous owner and is situated over the family room. You guessed it, if I want to change the temperature in the bedroom prior to installing the Nest I would have to truck downstairs to the family room to do so, now I just open my app and adjust as needed.

Nest is one of the largest players in the smart home

thermostat market place and also has cameras, smoke & CO (Carbon Monoxide) detectors, doorbells, alarm systems. If can be controlled from anywhere, will turn itself down when you are away and will save energy. Nest is owned by Google and ties into Google Home but also ties into the Amazon Alexa. Currently, Amazon and Google are in a battle over the smart home and Nest is right in the middle. We will have to wait and see how this all plays out. Some of the other manufacturers for you to look at are, Ecobee4, Honeywell Lyric T5 and the Lux TX500U.

Besides comfort and ease, these smart thermostats can learn when your home and when you're not, and say you energy by turning down when not needed. They also can be changed remotely to get the chill off the house before coming home from work.

Smart Plugs are an interesting item. We have changed most of our outlets out to have a USB charger (this can charge your tablet or phone) in each, it's fairly inexpensive and ensures that you can charge whatever you need to in the house. The smart plugs take this to the next level. Basically, it's a plug on your outlet that you then plug your appliances into. These smart plugs can turn the item on and off but mostly the monitor energy consumption. Fibaro, Wemo, TP-Link are smart plugs that tie into a larger smart home system. The plugs range from 30 – 60 dollars, while they say they will help you to save energy, at 60 dollars per plug plus the cost of command center, that's quite a bit of energy they will have to save to give you the value for your investment, however it would be awesome to know what is using the most energy and then having the tools to manage it.

**Safety and Security**

Safety and Security are interesting categories. People often confuse the two but, in reality, they are quite different.

Security keeps you free from danger or threat, while safety is when a product is designed to prevent damage or injury.

One, is responding to an outside force and the other is preventing damage or injury by design. Still confused? I feel the same way, for example, a shower grab bar to help you steady yourself and keep you from falling is an item that falls under safety. A lock on your front door is a security item, if you don't lock the front door you will not injure yourself, but you could be injured or harmed by someone that wants to enter your home to rob you. You don't need to worry about which is which, it really doesn't matter. What matters is these products provide peace of mind and freedom, two of the most valuable items on this earth.

## Security

When it comes to security, I am certainly not an expert, I do lock my car and the house at night, but I have yet to install cameras and smart locks on the doors. Our family has been way more safety oriented, probably due to the fact that there is always someone home and very rarely is anyone ever alone.

**Ring** is a doorbell/camera system for your exterior doors that allows you to see who is there before opening the door or even getting out of bed. There camera systems are stylish, can have a spotlight, floodlights, alarms and motion sensors. They also have cameras in the home if desired and it's all connected to live security folks when you need them. Your neighbors can even be alerted so they can be on alert also if you choose to be connected. It's the next level of a neighborhood watch. A unique feature is that you can install it yourself. They can also integrate it with a smart lock system so that you can lock or unlock your doors from home which can be convenient if you forgot to lock the door or unlock it for your dog sitter. Compatible lock systems are LockState, Kisi and Lockitron.

The family of **Nest** products include indoor and outdoor cameras, thermostats, doorbells, alarm systems, smoke and CO (Carbon Monoxide) alarms. Nest works with other products also like light bulbs, the washer and dryer, and door locks. An example they give of a smart connected home with Nest goes like this, your Smoke / CO alarm detects carbon monoxide. The nest system would then contact your furnace and shut it down as this may likely be the cause. They also do the traditional security sensors on windows and doors to keep you safe.

**Schlage Connect** – door hardware connects to Amazon Alexa via SmartThings, Wink, Iris or Nexia. It is a great exterior door lock system and when you connect it to your Alexa or other you can lock it or unlock it whenever you want to or need too. No more leaving keys for people, or your halfway to the movies and can't remember if you locked it or not, just lock it from your phone. It will even send an alert or an alarm if it's being tampered with.

**Iris** is unique in the security system arena as they focused not only on a connected home but helping latch key kids and seniors live safer. They have the cameras, indoor and out, the sensors, smart plugs, thermostats (Honeywell & Nest), but they also have an Iris Care Pendant and a Smart Fob. The Smart Fob is actually pretty smart, it has 4 customizable buttons that can turn on lights, lock the doors when you got home and even send a text to Mom that you got home safe. Think of it like a remote control for your house only pre-programmed. The Iris Care Pendant can be paired with sensors so that you can track if mom is ok, or it can even send you alerts if she has left the house. I know we could have used this the other day with my Grandma. She had never gone out the front door and wandered off but she did this morning and it was very cold and she said she was waiting for the school bus. Things change daily when you are living with dementia or Alzheimer's and now we have to lock the front door even when we are home. We may be looking into getting the Iris sooner rather than later. While it does not have all the bells and whistles of the other motion sensor alarm pendants, having the system connected to the smart home devices is a win. Lowes has also done a fantastic job with their senior friendly bathroom products and I encourage you to check them out. Falls in the bathroom can mean surgery a trip to the short term rehab. At my age, anything I can do to preemptively avoid having this happen and give me confidence as I age is a must do. Don't wait until you have an accident to install these safety products.

**ADT** has been around forever, we even had them at one point but then we got rid of our land line and they were not able to work without it. It was quite the order to get out of the contract but from my latest interview with them, things have changed. They have become very flexible, which is great news for you and me. They have the locks, sensors, key Fobs, cameras, app, and personal support. They, like Lowes Iris, have added a Senior and Health addition. They now have a medical alert system with fall detection and GPS. It's definitely not the prettiest but when did pretty mean good? Ok... Apple proved me wrong but you get what I mean.

**Frontpoint** is a DIY (do it yourself) security company with great customer service. They have cameras, sensors (these can also be on cabinets and drawers). They work with Schlage for the smart locks and also offer flood sensors. Best of all the system is portable so it can move with you.

**Vinint** They have a camera doorbell, cameras for inside and out, sensors 24×7 video recording, thermostats that help with energy management, garage door control and 24 x 7 monitoring. They also have live video and it works with Amazon Alexa.

**Protect America** integrates with Amazon Dot so you can use it hands-free. They have the standard sensors, cameras, motion detectors, and smoke detection. They provide 24/7 monitoring and have a smartphone app. They are a security company.

**Live Watch** is 10x faster in an emergency with their response times per their website. They have a Plug&Protect system that can serve up to 40 security and smart home devices such as smart locks cameras, thermostats, sensors, detectors, etc. Their basic system comes with door sensors, motion sensors, and 24/7 monitoring.

**SimpliSafe** looks like a smart home security system. It is well designed and could be confused for an aromatherapy diffuser or Google Home. They have various package sizes which can include anything from the base kit with a keypad and sensors, motion sensors, panic buttons, freeze sensor, water sensor, smoke detector, and cameras. It can detect intruders, and not confuse them with your pets. It has 24/7 support and ready right out of the box. As you can see not all products do all things, you have to go back to the questions below that discussed in the previous chapters to help you make the wisest decision for yourself.

**1. HOW ARE YOU GOING TO BE ABLE TO LIVE YOUR LIFE WITH FREEDOM AND CONFIDENCE?** In other words, how much technology will you let into your life, everyone has some sort of line in the sand that they draw, what's yours? Cameras inside or no cameras, GPS tracking devices on your keys and your phone so that you can find them easily? Weigh the pros and the cons. You probably do already in all aspects of your life today. I am willing to get patted down at the airport in order that I can travel. 30 years ago I would have said NO WAY! That would have been an invasion of my privacy and not worth it, but now I am like a cow going to a milking station....they tell me where to go, what to take off, they have sniffing devices that go through everything in my suitcase in front of everyone and then they pat me down like I am a prison inmate. And that all comes after I have been x-rayed! It's all relative what you will give up if you think what you're getting is better than what you are giving up. Technology and security are no different.

**2. WHERE WILL YOU BE LIVING YOUR LIFE?** Will you be at home a lot or traveling quite a bit, this could influence the type of system you have. If you have another house, I would invest in the same system for both properties so that you only have to deal with one app where you can have it all connected and monitored. If you spend part of the year in a sunshine state, are the freeze warnings and energy efficiency important to you?

**3. HOW ARE YOU GOING TO CARE FOR YOUR MIND, BODY AND SPIRIT?** Answering this question requires that you think really long, hard and carefully about future flexibility. You don't want to get locked into a system that can't grow with you as you age. On the other hand, you may want everything portable and not connected so that you can change what is not working well or if conditions change. Know your personality, if change is hard for you then select a system that will be around in the future, can grow with you and fits your level of learning new things.

**Safety**

On the subject of "Help, I've Fallen and I Can't Get Up" devices, there are so many devices out there and great information to help you stay connected if you or a loved one would need a safety device such as these. I believe in the not too distant future that these features will be integrated into the basic consumer wearables such as Fitbit, Garmin or Jawbone. As we saw with the new hearing aids, fall detection is part of the device. Wearables are currently starting to track more than your steps, heartbeat and sleep patterns, look for them to track your oxygen and sugar levels. Add in the AI for fall alert and we all will be wearing a device that provides constant feedback and alerts to help us to make better choices and get help when we can't ask for it.

While most have a range of pendants you wear around your neck, quite a few are moving to the watch model. It certainly is a better fashion statement and does not scream that I can't take care of myself. It's interesting to me why these devices are so popular, but then I have to remember that if my parents and grandmother did not live with me, I would worry, and this would be a great solution. When my grandmother fell and broke her wrist and hip, my mother was right there and so there were no worries about her laying there for hours by herself like other horror stories I have heard from my family and friends. However, I did notice the cloud of doom and gloom from so many.....Oh, she broke her hip, that's the number one cause of death in seniors over 65. Really is it? NO its not! According to the CDC in 2017, Heart

Disease, Cancer and Chronic lower respiratory disease are the leading cause of death by a mile. At almost 2 million deaths per year in 65 and older adults, only 2% are from unintentional injuries where Alzheimer's disease accounts for 5.5 %. However, the CDC also reports conflicting information and states that "falls are the leading cause of injury and death in older Americans" did you catch it? They have lumped death and injury together. So, in reality, their data does not conflict they have just sensationalized it, it still stands that 2% of deaths may have been the result of falls. I am not trying to belittle the issue, but the CDC has scared Americans to death, making seniors afraid to move for fear of falling when the exact opposite is true, we need to keep active to not fall. I wish I could issue a cease and desist for the CDC, most studies agree that being overly tired, over medicated, or our blood pressure dropping when we stand up are most of the reasons for falling, it's not the steps or being active.

My advice would be to take normal precautions when it's icy, turn the lights on when you're walking around at night, don't let magazines lay on the floor as they create a trip hazard and make sure cords are tied up. Doing these simple things will reduce the likelihood of a fall. But, it's soft drinks, potato chips and being a couch potato that is more of a danger to your health. Don't be afraid to be active.

Having preached for the last paragraph, I still recognize that these devices help with freedom and peace of mind, so let's do a quick rundown of some of the brands you may come across.

**Medical Guardian** has lots of options from pendants and watches to an all in one system, it can detect a fall, and has GPS to pinpoint your location and sensors in the home that can help keep the family aware and involved with alerts that are triggered. **GreatCall Wireless** and **Medical alert system**, the backbone behind Jitterbug cell phone that was designed for seniors has a smart screen, senior-focused apps and medical help, GPS and a 5Star Urgent response MobileHelp. Others are, **LifeStation, Helpbutton, Lifefone, Alert 1, Life Alert, Philips Lifeline** and **BeClose Senior Safety**. **Mynotifi** is a simple wristband that notifies loved ones when you fall through an app on their phone with a one time payment. The App also has mobility exercise to help keep you active. You can also ask for help by touch the band or it uses AI algorithms to detect if you have fallen and will notify others, best of all its waterproof.

You may be thinking...I thought this book was for me, a Boomer? This sounds like a bunch of stuff for old people or my parents. Well, according to the National Institute on Aging 1 in 3 people fall over the of age 65. Of the 77 million Boomers in the US, (according to AARP) seven Baby Boomers are turning 65 every minute. So my bet is some of you will find this helpful, and if not for you, maybe a parent.

I try very hard to make sure that I place my phone, glasses, keys in the same place every night. This helps me not to lose them. When I get lazy and don't follow my ritual, it can be a day or so before I find something which is very frustrating. It just happened to me with my winter gloves. I thought they must have fallen out of the car because I was sure I searched everywhere for them and they had disappeared. I have done this often enough that I no longer blame others as I know I probably misplaced them. Where did I find my gloves? In a bag in the trunk of my car, right where I put them.... Apparently, other people also have my issue and there are plenty of companies that want to help us out. They call these trackers and they basically hook (think of a keychain attached to your keys) to the item that you deem important enough and then when you can't find it, these trackers will help you locate it through GPS or making a sound. I actually bought them for my parents and then we tied it into the Amazon Alexa, when my mom can't find her phone she can say to Alexa, please ring my phone and Alexa does it. It's a pretty neat feature. On the GPS locations, they are not sophisticated enough to pinpoint the exact location, but you can see if you left it at work, a friend's house, in the car or in the house. Just don't expect it to tell you which room.

**The Kitchen**

The kitchen can be one of the most creative, fulfilling, drudgery, heart of the home spaces depending on one thing...you. It's a necessary part of every house, just like the bathroom whether you love it or hate it. If you're a gadget geek or foodie you're going to love some of the latest technology for the kitchen. I've also got some products to discuss to make it safer. On a side note, make sure you have a smoke and CO detector.

Let's start on the safety side, making sure the house doesn't burn down is always a good thing. Even if your memory is fine, we are so distracted and used to doing ten things at once. I know that when I am cooking, I will start other things like the wash, while I'm also looking at my phone or watching something on my tablet. I walk in and out of the kitchen and next thing I know there's something burning. Recently, I had water on the stove to help add moisture to the air, a big pot. I apparently forgot to fill it up before going to bed and yes, I could have burned down the house. A product like **Fire Advert or Intelligent Stove Safety** is what saves the day (or night) in these kinds of instances. They hook to your stove and either by a timer or the smoke detector going off will shut off the stove. Think of the peace of mind, especially if you live by yourself.

**Cool Tech and Foodie Products for the Kitchen (just a few):**

**Pantelligent** is a smart frying pan, which helps teach you how to cook. The pan tracks temperatures and adjusts cooking time automatically. It will send you a notification via an app to let you know when it's time to flip your meat over. It will even keep you from burning food.

**Drop** is a smart scale, it allows you to do several helpful things. It will weigh ingredients as you add them. If your low on an ingredient the app will adjust the recipe for you. It can also help you to make the perfect cocktail. This changes how we will shop, we won't need to buy more than we need and we will be able to use more of what we have without having to see food go bad, based upon this alone it's very smart technology. If you have downsized, you may not have the storage in your kitchen you used too and the Drop will help you to not have to have that extra bag of flour.

**Paragon** is a portable induction cooktop that can cook almost anything, of course it comes with a mobile app that allows you to set the temperature. It can steam cook, fry, basically anything you need. One of the really neat features is that is can hold your food at the right temperature until you are ready to serve it. Induction cooktops are like what the electric stove was, they will be the future as they are portable, safe and free up your counter space. The only drawback is that they require new connected cookware.

**June** is an intelligent oven that can toast bake broil & roast it has a built-in camera and can give your phone updates, it's the size of a microwave, temperature probe to make sure meat is done perfectly.

**Samsung Family Hub** is a computer, personal assistant and refrigerator all in one! The hub allows you to see what's in your fridge from your phone, set expiration dates for groceries and get notifications, create shopping lists, have a family schedule, write notes to the family with a whiteboard function, listen to music or watch movies... but the best part is it can order groceries from Instacart and works with the Alexa. With its three built-in cameras that snap a photo every time you close the door, it allows you to just look at the phone app when you can't remember what you had in the fridge while you are grocery shopping.

**Egg Minde**r is a simple egg tray that holds 14 eggs and tracks how many are in it. LED lights next to each egg will tell you which ones are the oldest, so you can use them first. You can look at – you guessed it, the app when you are shopping to see how many eggs you might need for that recipe. This product is from Quirky GE – products invented by real people (another example of crowdsourcing).

**Orange Chef Prep Pad** is a smart food scale with nutritional balance based upon weight, to make better eating choices – yes it has an app. Not sure what I would do with this but I am sure you foodies get it.

**Smart Thermometer** by Williams Sonoma is an oven tech probe that can be used alone or with an app so you're not tied to the kitchen while you're cooking. It also helps you to make sure the meal is perfectly timed and cooked. I have to admit I don't think I have ever used a thermometer while cooking but it sounds like a great idea.

**Hapifork** helps you to eat slowly, think of a sonic toothbrush but in a fork. The smart fork reminds you to slow down if you are eating to fast to eat mindfully by vibrating or lighting up. And yes it comes with an app and gamification. It can even go in the dishwasher.

**The Drop** helps you to be a better baker or just make it easier. Personally, I could use this as I am not much of a baker due to the face you have to measure exactly and follow directions. I am more the through it together type of cook. It works with your Ipad and is connected to its scale. They have online recipes, the tools you need. Another interesting feature is that it will scale your recipe if you don't have the exact amount of ingredients and even replace items if you don't have any of, oh say eggs around, saving you from that trip to the grocery store for 2 eggs but nothing else.

**HestanCue** has smart cookware with induction cooktops, recipes, videos all in the app. Perfect for parties or everyday cooking. Mobile induction cooktops, like this one, allow you to carry your kitchen with you, wherever you are living. IKEA even has one for camping.

**Panasonic Smart Kitchen** is a future item for the US but already available in Japan and Canada. Maybe it's a metric thing? They have some of the coolest storage items for a kitchen that I have ever seen, allowing you to double your storage capacity and have the items you use all the time in high cabinets that easily open and drop to arms reach. I am certainly trying to get them to come to the US so stay tuned.

**Kessbohmer** has some similar products to the Panasonic Smart Kitchen called iMove. iMove is a shelving system that allows you not to have to use a stool to get into the upper cabinets, it has a bar inside the upper cabinet that you can pull down and it lowers all the upper shelves to within reach.

**Legrand *the adorecollection*** is an incredibly well-designed smart under cabinet lighting system that is way more than just lighting. Imagine all those ugly outlets, you know the ones... that are in your beautiful tile or granite between your upper kitchen cabinets and countertop can now be gone! Easier to clean and more beautiful to look at, besides the fact that the one outlet you have means the coffee pot has to be in the wrong place and moved every time you cook dinner. Legrand has solved these issues by putting all the lighting and electric on a bar right up under the upper cabinets. The electrical outlets can be moved around as needed, so in case your countertop appliances change you don't have to have cords strung all over, just relocate the plug. The other great aspect of this bar is that you can get accessories to hold your iPad, tablet, smartphone, etc. that can also can be moved easily. Now your countertop is flexible and free and clear of clutter.

**Future Kitchen tech soon to release:**

**Frigondas** sounds like a dinosaur or something from a Godzilla movie. But it's really more like the movie Transformers.... Just like in the movie where the cars seem like they are just cars but then turn into these huge alien robot things (they are good huge alien robot things) the Frigondas looks like and acts like a microwave until you find out it can cool and freeze food in minutes. This is a great appliance if your downsizing.

**The Bathroom**

Bathroom technology revolves around three main things:

comfort, safety and independence, and all while trying to make sure you don't feel vulnerable.

Let's look at comfort first, as you may be familiar with the comfort items as they can be found in most master baths of multi-million-dollar homes. But, as we age, these become less luxuries and more desired necessities. Take for example a heated floor, as we age, we get up more often in the middle of the night. That shock to our system as our feet hit the cold tile and chills our whole body? A heated floor can help to ease the transition from bed to the bathroom. A towel warmer and a heat lamp are both wonderful to have and helps you keep your body temperature warm as you get out of the shower. As we age, you can lose up to 70% of your body fat which helps to keep you warm (insulated). And so when you get out of the shower your core temp will drop and it's much harder to get it back to normal. These simple little things do make a huge impact on our comfort as our bodies age.

Consider mounting an amber Led strip (on a sensor) on the bathroom door to easily see it in the night and orient yourself up. This will help to reduce falls as you won't be looking down at a night light. You can also the light in the bidet as a night light.

If you want to get a fan and motion light together, ISO Humidity Activated Fan and Exhaust Light is a great product that is ultra-silent, has a bright overhead light and a motion sensor activated night light made by Quirky GE.

What else should you do? Definitely add an anti-scald device to your showerhead and faucet. These typically won't let the temperature get over 117 degrees and help to keep the body safe due to less fat to protect us from water that is too cold or too hot.

Also, add USB outlets so that you can charge your phone or tablet when you're in the shower or watching the news while you are getting ready. These can cost as little as 10 bucks if you go with a smart plug your looking at 25.

Replace your toilet paper holder with a Grabcessories. It's basically a grab bar built into the toilet paper holder with great grips on the back. It's perfect for helping you to further steady yourself right where you need it: your center of gravity. They also carry lots of other items.

Living with your parents can sometimes means you see things you can't unsee.... One morning I was running late and by the time I left for work, my father was up (typically he is not). When I came out of my bedroom suite, apparently he thought he was alone and forgot to close his bathroom door because there he was in all his glory standing at the bidet toilet seat with his hands on the wall to steady himself going to the bathroom. While I never will be able to shake that image, it got me thinking and researching fast! That's how I found a great product by

Grabacessories, it's a grab bar shelf mounted over the toilet for gentlemen to steady themselves while they are going to the bathroom. It helps them and it keeps their wives from complaining about the handprints on the wall, this is what we call a real win-win.

36.5 million rolls of toilet paper, that's how much Americans use each year. The cost to create this toilet paper to the environment is huge and accounts for 15 million trees. If you have ever used a bidet as they do in Japan, Europe, and other countries make you feel like your stuck in the dark ages when you come back home to the method of "cleaning" Americans use – TP or toilet paper, paper, paper, paper – no water involved just dry tree pulp.

The best way I can explain my feeling for the bidet goes back to a story I told in my earlier book HIVE in a chapter called, Royal Flush. In 2007, I had a chance to travel to Japan for an Entrepreneurs Organization (EO) conference. Typically, I don't bring my family on business trips, but EO is different; they support the whole entrepreneur and encourage spouses to come along – sometimes even kids. Since family trips Cini Style also means taking my parents along, I mentioned to everyone that, "Japan would be an awesome trip for us all to go on." Immediately, Grandma, then 86, piped up with an enthusiastic, "I've always wanted to go to Japan!" Frankly, I didn't even have her on the guest list, but it seemed like a once in a lifetime event that I couldn't possibly deny. And so the entire family, Grandma, my parents, my husband and kids (ages 10 and 13) flew off to Japan for what proved to be "an awesome trip," and all of us treasure the memories of it to this day.

Now, what does this have to do with toilets?

Well, a lot, actually. While there, every toilet we experienced, even the public ones, had bidet seats on them that provided great comfort, greater cleanliness, and had a remarkably wide range of options. Among the options: a heated seat, a hidden wand that, at a touch of a button, would spray you off, and then, when you pressed another button your bum would be blow-dried. In simple terms... these toilets were frickin' awesome and we were frickin' impressed.

Arriving back home, I did some research and guess what Santa (me) bought Greg for our master bathroom that Christmas?

Now, back to Christmas season where I was waiting and waiting... for weeks...for the bidet. And nothing. I waited more and still nothing. Then I tracked the package and saw that a neighbor had signed for it.

A little background information. Not long before our Japan trip, we'd moved into a National Historic residence neighborhood. The kind that was gated and you have to be voted into. If you don't get my drift, think of it like this: most of the neighbors weren't baking pies and showing up to say: "Howdy, folks, welcome to the neighborhood" but they were signing for my bidet.

Great, now their first impression of me was going to be the kook who came ringing their doorbell to ask if they'd signed for, and forgotten to give me, my toilet seat from Japan. And well, yes, that's exactly what their first impression was because that's exactly what I did. And yes, they had it, and yes, it was as awkward as you can imagine. Not that it mattered, because when Christmas came, and we installed the seat, Greg loved it.

And then the weirdness came. That's right, what you read above was not weird. Pretty soon, every single friend of my kids who came over to the house would, when they had to use the bathroom, traipse upstairs, walk into my bedroom, and yep, you got it...beeline into my master bathroom and use our toilet. It didn't end there. Whenever we had a party, which we often did, we noticed the same exact phenomenon happening. Did I mention that we have 3 other common bathrooms? Yet everyone felt completely comfortable entering our master bedroom to get to the master bathroom toilet. When I happened to mention this to my friends, I was surprised by their reaction: they knew all about it. Turns out the "Cini toilet" was the talk of the town.

A few years later, we decided to sell that home and begin our new multi-generational lifestyle. And while we didn't know a lot of the details regarding what was going to happen, we did know one thing: the 4Gen Experiment would include many bidet toilet seats that could wash and blow-dry. But I have to admit, it was not just because I loved my bidet toilet seat and all its neighborhood acclaim; there was a different reason, too, which was lying in the answer to this question: How can I avoid having to wipe my parents bum if they have surgery or something happens to them? It's not as strangely hypothetical as it might sound. When my mother-in-law had surgery, my sister-in-law had to help her go to the bathroom, which also meant helping clean her – embarrassing for my mother-in-law, and tough on Greg's sisters. So when I thought about that not having that happen to me, my next thought was about the bidet toilet seat. And at $350.00 per toilet, it seemed like a small price to pay for their dignity and my sanity. And not just mine, but for my mom's too, who was to be the primary caregiver for my grandmother.

After she settled in from the big move, and our Social Experiment was up and running, one day I asked Grandma if my mother had shown her how it worked and how she liked it. I don't know why, but I was shocked to hear that she loved it! I didn't remember that Grandma, 93 at the time, was completely able to understand it and use it all by herself. I'd forgotten that she was no virgin to technology and that she'd seen more changes in technology than any of us; the development of new-fangled things such as the car, indoor plumbing, radio, TV, phone, cell phone, electricity, and the Internet. When you think about it like that, really, would a toilet that could wash and dry you be such a big deal?

And she had a reason that she liked it, too: it let her take care of herself, without being a burden on my mother. With her shower, she needed help, but the toilet seat allowed her to (basically) take a "sitz bath." My age group doesn't quite get this concept, but for folks her age, this is what they grew up doing; water was either collected in a rain barrel, or from a well or sometimes, if you had the luxury, the city got water to you. Regardless, water was not something you could waste. Women would often use a sitz bath for "personal hygiene", so this wildly new contraption (in our minds) was in a sense, incredibly familiar to her.

The bidet has fans and other options, too. I remember, with absolute clarity (and delight) the first time my father, a combination of Robert De Niro and Archie Bunker, used his bidet seat. Since he did not exactly read the manual from cover to cover, he went in and a moment later came out screaming that he had a "G.D. tornado up his A." After some quick coaching on the settings, he turned his way down from "high" and very soon he, too, came to love the bidet toilet seat. Grandma did not have the same model as my father. We were testing out different manufacturers on each toilet to see our likes and dislikes. I can honestly say, I am not sure why the setting "Vortex" should ever be on one of these bidet toilet seats, but my father was the lucky one to try it out.

My daughter's graduation party speaks to the bidets widespread appeal. Since we had several hundred guests, we rented port-a-potties. Guess what happened anyway? I had parents coming to me and asking if they could use the toilets inside because they had heard so much about them. It's a weird conversation to be sure, but it also goes to show how amazing they are.

Since our Social Experiment started, we have finally been able to convince some of our senior living clients to put them in their apartments! The lesson here is that with a small dollar investment you can increase the dignity and independence of your loved one and reduce your burden.

The positives end up being for everyone, which is a huge win-win. Update, I would also highly recommend getting the Squatty Potty, it's like a step stool for #2 which helps you to avoid straining yourself and getting hemorrhoids. Yes, it's official, I am an adult, I have talked about all of the bodily functions without even one giggle. I know this all may sound crass, but denial is not wisdom. When we can arm ourselves with strategies that are proactive we can age with confidence and freedom.

## Lighting

Candles were the main source of lighting during non-daylight hours for centuries. Oil, gas and kerosene lamps created a more stable source of light, but still needed maintenance and could be very dangerous. It was not until the 1930's when the incandescent light bulb became a mainstay in American homes in major cities, but in rural areas only about 10 percent of homes had electricity. By 1939, 25 percent of rural homes had electricity. Even with the low percentage in the rural areas, incandescent light bulb technology forever changed the way we worked and lived. We were no longer dependent on the sun; our work days could be longer and factories could add second and third shifts instead of building more factories.

In 1939, my grandfather left Canton, Ohio, to work the World's Fair in New York City. He would tell us stories of all of the movie stars and famous people he saw when they came through his "guess your weight" stand while at the fair. It was the place to be. It was branded as "Dawn of a New Day" and had an exposition of "The World of Tomorrow." TVs were introduced there, as well as nylon, color photography, air-conditioning, and fluorescent lamps.

GE held the patent to the first electric bulb. In the next

three years, electric bulbs were being produced by many companies and were installed in many manufacturing facilities and open office plans. Not until 1980 did compact fluorescent lights (CFLs) become available to retrofit into the same socket as an incandescent light.

While enough lighting is crucial to see, aging eyes require up to 70 percent more light to see than a 20-year-old. If you have ever been to a restaurant with your friends and everyone pulls out their cellphones and turns on their flashlight app to be able to read the menu, you know what I am talking about. The details are just as important: color temperature, not having bright spots or shadows, reducing the amount of fluorescents due to the eye strain caused by flickering (you may not be able to see it, but the eye still has to adjust), and consistency. Lowering the light levels can make it more difficult to see steps, chair seats, and handrails, which causes more stress and fear in you.

Factor in that every individual sees differently with colors and light levels and then throw in for good measure sight issues such as yellowing of the cornea, macular degeneration, nearsightedness, and farsightedness. This is why good lighting is so critical as you age.

**LED Lighting**

LED lighting technology has moved faster than expected, with GE and Phillips both moving at the speed of light to develop this technology and bring the price structure down.

The exciting news on LEDs is that they are now cost effective enough to use in homes. LED lights have been integrated into handrails in showers, door casings, and crown molding, and can change colors to help simulate sunrise, daylight, and sunset to help those with cognitive difficulties.

When LED uplighting is utilized in crown molding in your home, it can be used to simulate the natural light changes from day to night. The lighting is controlled by a computer connection that will sequence sunrise, daytime, sunset and then goes off at night. This simulation can help with your circadian rhythm, increasing the melatonin production to reduce sundowners, especially for those with SADD, Alzheimer's and dementia.

It was suggested to me by a doctor to add blackout window treatments in the bedroom to ensure that not too much light can seep into the room at night for the best possible night's sleep. I have also found my personal experience substantiates a better night rest when the room is dark if you live in the country with very little city lights pouring in at night this is not much of an issue except for full moons. Please take into consideration that when you do "blackout" your room you will definitely need amber night lights, so you don't kill yourself making your way to the bathroom in the middle of the night.

LEDs integrated into flooring, handrails, stairs and door casings help reduces tripping and falling. These integrated lights can double as nightlights and should be colored amber to avoid keeping you up at night as mentioned above. Elio's LED handrail system shown in the image can not only bear the weight of you and be easy to find when your eyes are full of water but also provide a night light for the bathroom.

Imagine this scenario, the rooms in your house automatically lighting up when you enter because it is tied to motion sensors; the uplighting in the crown molding around your room is the same color temperature as the hour of the day and therefore will change throughout a 24-hour period.

The door casing (amber-colored) is lit to help orient you navigate at night to minimize the risk of falling, creating a holistic lighting solution that allows your smart home technology to give your confidence and be as free as possible. Kohler introduced many integrated lighting solutions into their bathroom products just this year.

An LED light over the toilet comes on when you approach it and gets brighter as you get closer. You may also have, like I do, a night light in my bidet toilet, I have to say I did not think it would really help but it does, and I would insist on having them if I ever moved. Inside the shower and beside the toilet are integrated LED-light handrails that make it easy for you to see, especially when your eyes may have water or shampoo in them.

For getting out of the shower, a water-resistant LED light strip helps to define where the flooring change is to avoid trips and falls. Then, back to the bed, where the sensors lower the light levels back down till you are safely in bed and off to restful sleep. In the morning the LED cove lighting gently awakens you with the warm colors of a sunrise, the theory is, that provided this cuing, the body's circadian cycle will be properly set and poor sleep and sundowner's syndrome could be diminished, if not avoided.

Great smart lighting that is not only bright but even and flexible with color and dimming capabilities all connected to sensors and your smart home technology lets you create mood and improve quality of life. Who doesn't like a sunny day vs. a cloudy one?

**OLED Lighting**

OLEDs (organic light-emitting diodes) are different than LEDs (light emitting diodes). The major difference that matters is OLEDs are can be extremely bendable, thin and even translucent. They are also better in color, which translates to not only better lighting but better, thinner, curved TV's, phone display and computer screens.

There are numerous simple ways that OLED smart lighting can be applied to your home. A few examples are: under cabinet lighting, closet lighting, bathroom mirrors with built-in lighting, stair tread lights, toilet seats with built-in lighting, vanity mirrors, cove lighting, ceiling panels and hanger lights.

OLED's will be as great a transformation as the light bulb was to the candle.

Some high-end restaurants have clued into aging eyes to ensure their guests keep coming. I experienced this myself in a fancy restaurant in Germany. They used OLED technology behind the menu, which backlights the menu, so it was easy to see, it only comes on when you opened the menu up. It was incredible, no struggling, no almost catching the menu on fire because I came too close to the table candle.

If you have cataracts, then it is difficult to see in bright light and you should avoid glare. You can see the dilemma, right? One spouse needs the lights bright and the other needs it not too bright. This is the exact reason you should use smart home lighting. You can set them to your preferences just light you do in your car for the seat adjustments. I am 4'11 and my seat and steering wheel is set very differently than my husband's (he is 5'10). It used to irritate me to no end when we had a car that did not have these programmed positions. I would have it perfectly set for me and then he would change it and then it seemed like I could never get it back to where I had it perfect again. Smart Home technology is a lot like a luxury vehicle that adjusts to your preferences, helps to protect you with airbags and sensors, locks and alarms, guides you with GPS (it may even parallel park for you), creates the perfect comfort level for you in temperature and allows you to easily communicate with whoever you want all while doing its primary function of providing you the freedom to go where you want when you want.

When you're buying your smart lights from **Lifx, Phillips, GE,** etc look for a CRI (color rendering index) of 80 or higher. The range is from 1-100 and the higher the number the more accurate the colors you will see. The better the colors, the better you, your food and your environment looks.

## Protect yourself

When everything is connected, everything is connected... Just like you protect your car, diamonds, and money you need to protect your system from Hackers (they are basically like internet bad guys), there are many ways to keep the hackers away but they are each tailored to what system you have in place and if you want to hook something up yourself or hire a professional.

Password protect is key but it's not enough, when you are connected via Wifi having passwords that are easy to guess can leave you vulnerable.

## WELL Building

Heres an interesting concept that gathering steam. So much so that it's really becoming a movement now. It's called Well Building and it's moving past the Green movement and LEED-certified buildings. "Back in the day" which was not that far back, the concept of Green or LEED-certified buildings was to help to protect the environment and reduce energy consumption. It did this by sourcing local materials, utilizing the position of the building as compared to the sun to reduce the heating and cooling systems so you don't have to fight against nature. Mother Nature always wins, so it's better to work with her than against. You also need to use local plants that require less maintenance and irrigation and so on.

The Well Building Standard considers the environment, but it focuses on those of us living in that environment as well, neat concept right. What if the air quality, light, and water in your home or workplace actually made you healthier and allowed you to live a better, more engaged life. With 90% of our time spent indoors, the WELL Living Lab in collaboration with the Mayo Clinic is researching just how to do this and how our environments may assist in our wellbeing.

When asking President of Delos Commercial Phil Williams, the company that created the WELL Building Standard what is at the heart of having a WELL building he stated "Right or wrong, every generation is spending 90+% of our time inside buildings. The places where we now live must and can move from "do no harm to great". This applies to the physical place, the cultural place, and our personal place."

## Universal Design

In Senior Living, the US government makes designers like myself comply with ADA (Americans with Disability Act) when designing our large purpose built senior living facilities. The problem is that while they are well intentioned just like the CDC, they are actually, in some cases, making it more difficult for aging adults to thrive and unfortunately this has found its way into our aging in place environments as well. To understand the issue, you need to know how ADA came about, it was not for aging adults. It came out of the Vietnam vets coming home with limb loss and great upper body strength, most were males between 18-21 so I am told. So it made perfect sense to design a grab bar that was similar to what the Olympic gymnast use, think of it, the still rings, parallel bars, pommel horse and the high bar. All of these revolve around gripping a bar and then swinging your body around by the strength of your hands, arms and upper body. What's the issue? were not 18-21 years old and most of us don't have great upper body strength. Throw in arthritis which makes it difficult to grab something in the shape of a tube. This is why a round doorknob is more difficult to turn when you have arthritis than a lever door handle.

So what can we do? Intro, please...... meet Universal Design, it's similar to WELL in that it looks at the whole picture and figures out the best options versus being prescriptive for one group or another. Universal Design works for everyone not just those in a wheelchair, although it works for that too. If your aging in place, downsizing or designing a new house, look for universal design elements, you'll be glad you did.

There are seven principals in Universal Design, but what it really comes down to is common sense, can you make an environment simple and intuitive, able to be used with low physical effort and it accommodates people of all sizes and abilities.

As you may have figured out by now, in order to know what really works for me or not, I'd really rather be living in my environment than figuring it out by being "book smart". When I wrote HIVE, The Simple Guide to Multi-generational living, I was able to help others because we were living in our social experiment and that meant that some of what I thought of as brilliant ideas at the time just plain old flopped. When I wrote about these, I followed my mentor Dan Sullivan's advice to "focus on progress, not perfection".

While I had employed some universal design aspects to our home, I found that the better source for my information (and inspiration) happened to be right here in my town, living in her own living laboratory of universal design. Her name is Rosemarie Rossetti (now age 65), and her life changed on June 13, 1998. That was the day that a 3 1/2 ton tree came crashing down on her. She became paralyzed from the waist down at age 44. In her interview with me she told me that when she returned home from the hospital, she quickly realized that her home was working against her, not for her.

She's an incredible, smart woman so let's start there. Some would say she has taken lemons and turned them into lemonade but really, she made lemonade for the world. She told me it's really about having a resiliency mindset. And she is on a mission to help others "make their life easier," she looks at everything and asks what she calls the 4 Mores:

- What will make my life more convenient?
- What will make my life more safe?
- What will make my life more independent?
- What will give me more peace of mind?

While I won't be able to go through everything she stands for and advocates for in this book, please look her up on the internet and see all the great data, tools and resources she has. She with the help of her husband Mark and lots of wonderful vendors built an environment where Rosemarie trials out products similar to what we did in HIVE. And so, Rosemarie really spoke from the heart about what worked and what did not. She is part of the inspiration behind the Limitless Living Manor House.

If your a younger Boomer, born around 1964 you may not think this applies to you, but hear me out. If you are planning on aging in place which 90% of you are then figuring out how to renovate the home you are in, or downsizing to a new house or condo or even buying a new house should have you thinking about what can you do to allow the environment to work for you not against you, as you age. The time a crisis happens is not the time to be figuring this all out. Plan now. Ensure your future freedom.

Now we will return back to your previously scheduled HGTV show, lol (laugh out loud). One of the first things you will notice is that the space is more open than a normal house, doorways especially. Pocket doors and barn doors are used wherever possible so that the floor space is not taken up by the door and the opening is as wide as possible. When you use a normal 30" door lets say, due to the hinges and the actual thickness of the door, you lose a couple of inches and this means you may really only get a 27-28" opening. For someone in a wheelchair or walker, this can mean the difference between fighting through every door opening and not.

Next, you would notice that the house is not built just for someone in a wheelchair. What? Shouldn't everyone have to accommodate the person with needs, even if it means they are less comfortable? Not necessarily, having a great living space means having a great living space for everyone in the home. Rosemarie is 5'1 standing and 4'2 in a wheelchair, Mark is six foot tall. Her kitchen is the perfect display of universal design. The island has three heights to it, 34" high for the workspace for Rosemarie vs normal 36" high cabinets, 30" table space for everyone including Rosemarie and others who might be sharing cooking duties in there.

All of the Kitchen cabinets are 34" high (the cabinets are Kraftmaid and you can get them standard at 34") as Rosemarie loves to cook and as mark says "he loves to eat". Some unique features are: that the upper cabinets are 14" above the counter top vs the standard 18" this helps her to access them from a seated position. The oven is below this 34" and has a side door like a microwave so it's easier for her to get her food in and out of because she is not blocked by the door.

I fell in love with the whole kitchen due to my height. At 4'11" and being 50 years old it's getting more and more difficult to vault up on the counter, and then precariously stand to open the cabinet doors and then jump to get down. I used to do it with ease but now when I am getting up and down I look like a gymnast doing the balance beam and I am very aware of the great pressure that comes from needing to "stick my landing" so I don't end up in a cast.

One of the unique features that I think we all can

appreciate and use as we age is Rosemarie's built-in steamer and drainer. She has this right next to her burners and beside a pot filling faucet. To explain a little better, it's very difficult for her to fill a pot with water then transfer it to the cooktop, then after the pasta is cooked, transfer the scalding water and pasta back to the sink and then pour the water into a strainer. Lots of opportunities to end up with a huge mess on the floor or worse yet a burn unit. With the layout and the steamer/boiler/drain well, she fills the pasta cooker utilizing the swinging faucet, then turns it on, puts in the pasta and then when it's done his the drain button! The pasta cooker looks very much like a sink but it actually cooks pasta and steams.

You can see how this smart appliance technology helps her with all of her 4 Mores, What will make my life more convenient, What will make my life more safe, What will make my life more independent and What will give me peace of mind.

Her unique bathroom pocket door, is not a door at all it's a privacy divider that goes into the wall and hides her on the toilet, should she ever need help in the future with transferring when she goes to the restroom, the pocket door can be slid into the wall opening up the floor space for someone to have room to help her.

## Future Planning

Future Planning is the process of proactively designing your home environment with elements that are not fully built out but make it easier to install in the future. It also allows gives you the confidence that if you need to install support items for aging in the future, adding them will be easy, but until then, you don't have to compromise your interior design aesthetic.

Imagine this, you want to be able to age in place but you're not ready to have grab bars in the bathroom yet. Future planning would be adding the blocking into the walls behind drywall or tile. Blocking provides stability to the wall so that heavy items do not pull out or loosen. When you install grab bars into normal drywall or tile, there is little to hold them past the ½" of material and with the amount of weight being placed on them they can loosen or even fall out of the wall which can cause serious injury. If you add blocking to the walls of your bathroom, staircases and even bedroom and bathroom ceilings prior to you needing to add the grab bars, this will future proof your home and you will not have to rip out all the walls to add blocking when you are ready to add grab bars. Grabcessories has solved this to a certain extent with their patented toggle bolt but it's still wise to have blocking.

Other things you can consider when future planning

besides blocking are: handrails at all stairs, outlets by the bedside, nightlights, electric by the toilet if you want a bidet toilet seat in the future, heat lamp and lower counters if you are renovating.

While these may seem insignificant, they can make an enormous difference in your freedom and quality of life, with much less cost and disruption when you decide to make the physical changes to your environment that will allow you to age in place.

Rosemarie has also future planned many items and has not compromised her design aesthetic in any fashion. She is a living example of how fantastic, supportive interior design can still be beautiful and tasteful.

## Biophilia

Biophilic Design encourages the connection between the inside and the outside. Research has found that we are happier, require less pain medication, sleep better and heal faster when we are connected to nature. When we are inside, this can happen through windows and artwork. Spending 90% of our time inside it's no wonder we desire to be connected to nature. That two-week vacation to the beach just won't cut it. Besides views of nature, biophilic design also encourages the dynamic use of sunlight, being able to hear and see water (a fountain, stream, lake, ocean), natural ventilation and the introduction of natural forms and materials into the interior home. This design technology fits perfectly with the WELL Building standards and universal design.

When all of these smart house options are pulled together, you can be confident that you can have an environment that will support your needs not only now but in the future. The key is future flexibility and understanding what is important to you and then tailor your home's solutions towards these goals.

# 12. The "LOVE" Design Method.

If by chance you read my book HIVE, *The Simple Guide to Multigenerational Living*, first let me say THANK YOU! Second, you will notice that this section comes from that book with some updates and tweaks. My first book *The Future is Here, Senior Living Reimagined, How Technology Will Change the Face of Senior Living in the Next Five Years* has also been borrowed from and updated for this book. It's basically a mashup of the past 5 years with lots of great new stuff. Now back to the LOVE Method.

As I have previously mentioned, my folks and my 96-year-old grandmother with dementia moved in with us several years ago. This social experiment forced me to think deeper on how I would execute memory care design in my own home without making the whole house institutional for the rest of us. What I discovered, was that great design works for everyone.

While you may not know someone with memory issues, the LOVE Method works for anyone. If you do have someone you love that suffers from memory decline, then please dig in, I know there's something that will help make their, and your, life easier and isn't that what love is all about.

When it came time for me to sit down and design

Grandma's apartment, I hit on an easy to remember design philosophy, which is remarkably similar to a life philosophy: "LOVE." Light, Optimize, Visual & Ease.

If you design with "LOVE", you increase independence and dignity. Designing with LOVE means you're allowing the person suffering from Alzheimer's/ Dementia to be their best them at that moment in time. And designing with LOVE gives you the flexibility to adapt to their ever-changing needs. That all sounds so positive and enlightened, but oddly enough, the LOVE Method caused a very non-loving response between all of my family. The LOVE Method caused me to argue with my siblings and parents about how to best design the environment for my grandmother. Today, four a half years since the renovation took place, and three and a half years of living in this social experiment, I can say that the **LOVE Method** works.

Some of what I implemented for Grandma was different than what I would do in an assisted living home design that we would create at my company, Mosaic Design Studio. Here, in my own home, I was able to experiment with what I felt would work best vs. what code requires when designing a commercial space for seniors. And Grandma's bedroom was one such place, where the minimum square footage requirements in senior living are much larger than the space I had to work with at our home.

Grandma's suite was designed to have a living room, bedroom, bathroom, and outdoor entry. We added large French and sliding doors to any outside wall possible. If there was a wall that was not connected to the inside of the house. This meant that, if it could have a window or door placed in it to the outside to bring in natural light, then we put them in. We were employing the first letter of the **LOVE** design philosophy, **L = LIGHT**. We put integral blinds into the French doors so that she would not get them all gibber jawed by playing with them. Integral blinds mean that the mini blinds are sandwiched in between the panes of glass. They can still be opened, closed raised up or down at any height. They are safe and do not need to be cleaned. We also placed a window in Grandma's bedroom. Since the brain's alarm clock is kicked off by light, which produces melatonin, the benefit of all this natural light was to help Grandma sleep normal, instead of having her waking up at all hours of the night. Natural light would also help cue her to the time of day. This would be a big help to early-stage Alzheimer/ Dementia folks, helping them to recognize the difference between breakfast and dinner and the appropriate time to go to bed.

A couple of hints: Make sure to close all the blinds/drapes at night so no outside light sneaks in. Actually, this hint is for everyone, it will greatly help your sleep and regulate your circadian rhythm. Now here's one I know might be hard but...NO watching TV, Tablets or looking at smartphones or screen devices one hour prior to going to sleep. The light emitted from these devices actually tells your brain to stay awake and screws up your circadian rhythm.

TV's are worse than phones and tablets and if you use those, use the nighttime lighting. Also, get a Human Charger and use it every morning. If there is one gadget besides the bidet toilet seat that is high on my list for everyone to improve their quality of life, this is it.

Light sensors are great. Definitely use them when you need them. As I've talked about, Grandma definitely needed them; she had five stairs off her Living Room, so to keep her safe we put a light sensor on them. It comes on automatically when it senses movement, which is great because we didn't have to worry about her remembering to turn on the light when she moved around. We also have a railing on one side of the steps and wanted to be sure she used it, which meant being sure she saw it. (It's not rocket science, most times its just common sense.) So rather than it being the same color as the wall and blending into the wall, we stained it so that it would contrast with the wall color. This makes the railing "pop," and she never missed seeing it!

Lighting has to be great in the bathroom, that's obvious, but my decision on "to dim or not to dim" was less obvious. Ultimately, I didn't put the bathroom on a dimmer. I didn't want there to be one more thing for her to have to mess with, and didn't think she needed yet another gadget to cause her confusion: a light switch that isn't quite a light switch? Or, wait, is it? See how easy it could be to get confused? So, I opted to use the amber colored night light to draw her into the bathroom, rather than a dimmer on the main bathroom light. Once inside, she sees a light switch, she hits it and it turns on, she hits it and turns off. It's clear to her. Sometimes the simplest is the best.

**O = OPTIMIZE** in the LOVE Design Philosophy. The bathroom space is optimized by only having what Grandma needed and nothing that she didn't. As in her bedroom which had a bed, nightstand, dresser and bench, this was done to reduce her confusion, stress and frustration. In the bathroom, our lack of space and need to remove obstructions caused us to use pocket doors (universal design feature) between her bedroom and bathroom. Having the pocket door to the bathroom open makes it easy to get in and, when open, creates the largest clear floor space for maneuverability and visual cuing. Not only does a "normal" door take up floor space, it's also one more thing for Grandma to manipulate around on the way to, and once inside, from the bathroom.

An easy example of how to optimize is by combining

multiple features into one item to save on space, cost, and function. In the bathroom, we have this in a combination: light, heat lamp and fan fixture, which doesn't come on automatically. It's located near the shower and she had to turn it on, but usually, it was my mother who did this for her, because Grandma was less independent and needed help showering. This is another place where you can take it up to the next step by adding a temperature control setting to make sure the water won't scald anyone. This is great whether you're coming in to check on your loved one once a day, or once a week.

We also added another optimized item which is a combo grab bar and toilet paper holder. The problem with most grab bars is that they place your hands so far back that your center of gravity is off and it's ok to help you steady yourself, but it's actually difficult when it comes to helping you get on and off the toilet unless you have great arm strength (most women have poor upper body strength). The location is perfect because it lets your center of gravity be in the right location, so you can easily get up and down with the least amount of effort. It's also smaller and looks better and what kind of interior designer would I be if all I cared about was function?

It's funny what you think of as "bells or whistles" when you're younger and how they become essentials when you're older, or at least designing for someone who's older. That was the case with something as simple as a heat lamp in the shower. As I mentioned earlier, getting older means losing about 70% of our body fat (this is why our skin starts to sag), and that fat is what's helping us maintain our body temperature, and it's also helping us get "the chill off." Coming out of her shower, Grandma would go from hot water/hot air to cold air relatively fast with very little insulation. The small addition of a heat lamp (this is the combo fixture) in the shower helped warm up the air for her, and let her step out into a warmer space. For the folks who don't want to take a shower anymore, making the bathroom a warmer, nicer environment is a little thing you can do to make it more enticing. While Grandmas bathroom did not have this, my bathroom has heated floors and a heated towel bar. I often get up in the middle of the night with no slippers or socks, which she would never do and these little items are a great comfort during our cold midwestern winters. These are not "essential" but they sure do make the bathroom experience more pleasant.

Grandma's shower had a curtain, not a glass door. Like most of the decisions I made for her, this, too, had specific reasons behind it. A glass door would make it difficult for her to get in and out. Also, since my mom was there helping Grandma shower, the glass door would restrict my mom's movements, making it harder for her to help. And then there was my biggest concern: what if she fell? The glass door could possibly shatter, and they could both be hurt. A curtain made a lot more sense. We were able to optimize the space to be large and less restrictive for my mother helping my grandmother by using a curtain vs. a glass door.

The third letter in the **LOVE** design philosophy is **V= VISUAL**. Visual is not just about seeing better, but also about visual cues, which are the brains highway signs to let you know that you are on the right path. The key idea here was separating the spaces as much as possible. I wanted Grandma to understand the reasons for the spaces, for their design to be apparent. Doing this would help her be less confused by her environment, or so I hoped. When she walked into her apartment, I wanted it to be easy for her to understand the purpose of each space and to know what to expect. If she did, it would help her be less agitated, again, "or so I hoped." With easily understood spaces would allow Grandma would to have a higher level of independence; she'd be able to enjoy moving from one area to another for specific reasons that would engage her, and the way they were designed reinforced their purpose. The key thought behind designing for a someone with memory issues is this: when dealing with people who are already confused, don't confuse them further by the interior design. Taking this to heart meant, for me, having Grandma's apartment work with her, not against her.

Even the things that seemed like mindless decisions need

more thought than you would think. Take towels for instance. Standard white, right? Easy and done. Except, think again. Grandma was old, her eyes were bad, and without her glasses, her world was a blur. Giving her towels that have color provided a contrast to her off-white painted walls. She was able to see her green towels easily without her glasses.

A simple and helpful idea for wall color is to paint the wet wall (the one the toilet is attached to) a brighter color, or accent color. This lets the toilet be clearly visible, and makes it so much easier for someone to see. And for men, it's even more important because they're standing up and aiming. Placing a grab bar behind the toilet at shoulder height allows a man to steady himself while urinating (in my family we say "peeing"). Putting an amber colored night light directly over the top of the toilet is another thing that helps them aim. In many bathrooms, handrails beside the toilet is a good idea. While we didn't need it because the sink is so close to the toilet that Grandma uses it to steady herself, My husband, Greg still added a handrail on the left hand side of the toilet.

Bathrooms are tricky places for the memory impaired, in the same way they were tricky places for small kids. Lots of things in there could be misinterpreted: liquids that don't look lethal but could be, powdery things that look harmless unless they're consumed, the creams, the ointments, the lotions, the colorful little pills—how do you design for all their needs and still keep them safe, yet as independent as possible?

If you're waiting for me to talk about the medicine cabinet in Grandma's bathroom, the wait will be a long one: there wasn't one. There was a mirror. But not a medicine cabinet. Every day, my mom came into Grandma's apartment with a little basket that had Grandma's meds and she gave them to her, eliminating the chance of any medicine cabinet mix-ups, toss-outs, or flush-downs. Things happen as the memory goes. As her symptoms increased, Grandma became more argumentative and a bit more paranoid. Some days she thought she already took her meds and that maybe she was being poisoned. In her heart, she knew she took them, and she was right, she did...but at another time. Soon we started seeing her hiding them, and soon after that, my mother started becoming more stern with Grandma to take them. Rather than getting into an argument, and saying, "No, you didn't" and Grandma would respond, "Yes I did " with all the attitude fit for a teenager, whereupon my mother would snap back and off it would go from there, eventually we just said: "Yes you did, but this is a new one." This is part of positive manipulation, which was needed to get her to take the medicine; it's telling her a different story.

The same goes for what you would normally have under your bathroom sink cabinet. I have an easy rule: "If you don't want them to take it by themselves, don't have it in there." So, cleaning supplies? Not going to be in there, where Grandma could possibly mistake it for something to drink. Medicine? Not going to be there. Mouthwash? If you drink it, it could be dangerous in excess, but toothpaste is fine. We only had pump soap for her to use for washing; bar soap can get slippery and flip out of her hands, and then she could have slipped on it. Sometimes employing the **V = VISUAL** in the **LOVE** method is as much about making sure you don't see certain things, to help a person be more independent and safe.

Visual cuing can also mean having items that are familiar. Grandma's bedroom had been familiar to her since way back to move in day, a day that was hard for all of us, but especially hard for her, with her strong reliance on visual cueing and familiarity. The thing we did here to help her bring her own bed and furniture; it helped her then and continues to do so to this day. She knew her items, her bed, her nightstand, her bedspread. They not only helped her to remember but also help provide her with the great comfort that familiarity brings. We all know that people have relationships to blankets and pillows. This starts early on in our childhood and never seems to leave us. You might be tempted to freshen up with a new look for your loved one's bedding, but I would advise against this. Keep as much as possibly familiar (even if it's a decorator's nightmare). Trust me, if I can do it, you can too.

And then there's her faucet: a one-handled one for Grandma. The pros outweigh any cons. It's a safety thing. With a faucet that has a separate cold and hot lever or knob that you have to turn on each and then blend the water to the right temperature, there's a risk. This goes against the 4$^{th}$ letter of the LOVE design philosophy: **E = EASE**. It's not easy to blend or even to remember the need to do so. The consequences could range from simple discomfort of the water being too cold to scalding herself with the hot water only turned on. With a one-handed faucet, there's a much smaller risk of her turning on the wrong one and scalding herself. There is one con to take into consideration, if someone has never used a one-handed faucet, they might be confused. You can add to the faucet a temperature controller to ensure that water that's too hot does not come out.

At the top of Grandma's stairs, we made another purposeful **E = EASE** design decision: we moved the door out to give her a three-foot landing. And so, whenever she was getting ready to open the door to go to the rest of the house, we didn't worry about her teetering on the top step before going in, or out. She would get to her landing, pause, get her footing, get her balance, and then move to where she needed to be. It's just a simple landing before opening the door, but it made a huge difference for her. In fact, just these few little things for her stairs: light, handrail contrast, the landing...made the steps so much easier for her to use. If we had made it difficult for her to use, she wouldn't have come into the rest of the house as much, and that's the opposite of what we wanted for her. This is a great example of the **E = EASE** in the Love Design Philosophy. We wanted her to be all around the house, engaging with us, not cooped up in her apartment all day. And so far, to a pretty great extent, we've succeeded.

What helped me wrap my head around the **LOVE** method was something I noticed about myself. I travel three to four days a week, and I noticed something: I often can't remember the layout of the hotel room when I am trying to find the bathroom in the middle of the night. I get up, am disoriented and sometimes I am the thing that goes "bump in the night." And yes, in more extreme cases, I'm the thing that goes bump and falls in the night. Though I don't have Alzheimer's/Dementia, I do have difficulty when in a new environment and just waking up. So, I reasoned that my grandmother who may not remember her bedroom layout may be just as disoriented as I get in various hotel rooms, perhaps even more. In nursing homes, it is common when someone is a fall risk to place their twin bed up against a wall. This would help them to not get trapped on the inside wall if they rolled out of bed. It also helped to create muscle memory, so we tried the same concept of only allowing her one option to enter and exit her bed. The intention of the design was to create **E = EASE** for my grandmother, reducing choices and creating muscle memory.

We also designed the bathroom space to have a shower with seat, a sink, and toilet with a bidet seat. It sprays, blow dries, and the seat is heated, some models even have nightlights, something to consider, too. The bidet let Grandma clean herself, or, if my mother was helping her in this department, it really helped reduce her efforts, and that was a nice plus for her. Once, after grandma came home from a short-term rehab following a surgery, I helped with her toileting and I can assure you, the bidet toilet seat is now my best friend and worth every penny. As I mentioned before, sometimes the things we may consider the bells and whistles, become necessities not only for a loved one's dignity but also for your sanity.

When I was in college in Dallas, Tx it was a world of difference from my small town of Canton, Ohio where I'd grown up. Driving on the Dallas super highways created a combination of fear, confusion and frustration on a daily basis. What I found looking back, was this was mostly due to the fact I was unfamiliar with where I was going, the system, and needing to make fast choices.

There was no GPS back then so trying to figure out on a 6 lane highway with exits to the right and to the left and signs all over, which lane I should be in when and which exit was mine and trying to get off in time would cause that burning feeling in my stomach. If I couldn't figure it out quickly then I would become paralyzed unable to make a decision, so then I would just drive along and soon I'd have to pull off to get my bearings.

Eventually, I figured out the system, but it got me thinking. My grandmother's life was a lot like being on a Dallas superhighway. Except she NEVER figured out the system. So how could we make her life have less panic, frustration, confusion, and fear? I remember driving on the highways in Canton, 2 lanes generally, with exits only on the right. Clear exit signs ahead told where to get off. When you see the exit you need, you get off at that exit. No fear, confusion or frustration. Then it hit me! **When you limit choices, you increase independence and confidence.**

One thing I didn't design into her bedroom was a closet. In part, it was due to space, but there was something else at work here, too. Every day my mother would lay out Grandma's clothes for her on her bed. This was another way of providing **E= EASE** in her decisions, and another way of helping her to be more independent. Dressing herself was a big part of Grandma's independence, and since we wanted that to happen for a long time, we did things like this to help encourage it to happen. By my mother laying out her clothes every day, Grandma had one exit sign to get off at. She didn't have to view a closet full of choices, deciding if pajamas should be worn for lunch or a dress for bedtime. She saw the clothes on the bed (one outfit) and my mother said, "Get dressed, mother," (get off at this exit) and my grandma could successfully get dressed with no stress.

There's another reason for limiting Grandma's choices. Let's look at her bed again. There it is against the wall. There Grandma was not making a choice in how she's going to get up, she's just going one way. So, not only did this help her get up without a hassle, but it also helped her start building muscle memory, which she could build vs. mental memory, which she couldn't build anymore and lost daily. No matter what our age, our body can build muscle memory, and it happens simply by doing the same thing every day in a way that becomes almost automatic. Ever sit down on a toilet at restaurant or airport and felt yourself drop? It's because your derriere is trained to a certain height, most likely the height of the toilet in your home, and you've built muscle memory that tells you how high and where to sit. I was always looking to improve Grandma's muscle memory, and making her daily choices repetitive and automatic helped accomplish that. Building muscle memory for getting in and out of bed is a great example of the "E" in the "**LOVE**" Design Philosophy.

This let Grandma get up to less confusion, which reduced some of her stress around decision-making. It's stress that comes from her wading through her life and wondering, "what do I do here, I don't understand."

Without a lot of decisions required of her, she was able to be more independent, less frustrated, less anxious and less agitated.

So though we didn't add all the bells and whistles, partly because we wanted the space to be able to grow with her as her needs changed and partly because we were on a budget, what we feel we did do was create a manageable "home" within our home for Grandma to live with as much independence and ease as possible.

Finally, the toilet, I actually have a whole chapter on this in HIVE so be sure to read it for all the details. I may have mentioned that I wanted to test some theories for those with Alzheimer's and Dementia that I have not been able to with my clients. The bidet toilet seat was one of those items. It's a seat that goes onto a conventional toilet and costs about $400.00. You need to have an outlet, which most bathrooms do. The toilet seat makes the seat height correct for a senior and is antibacterial and antimicrobial. It is warm, can come with a nightlight, and has a sprayer that can be positioned for various private parts, but it only sprays if someone is sitting on the seat. It is by far the largest success story of this whole 4-Gen Social Experiment. I was concerned that Grandma would not understand it, I asked her what she thought of it and she said at first, she did not know that it was anything special. However, after my mother showed her what it did, she loved it. She felt it was wonderful to be able to give herself a "sitz bath" and reduce the burden on my mother. My mom let me know on several occasions that if it were to ever break, it would be the first thing to be fixed. Even if Grandma could no longer remember to operate it properly, my mom's effort would have been substantially reduced compared to a regular toilet. I believe it is so successful because it engages all 4 of the 4 design philosophies in **LOVE: Light, Optimize, Visual and Ease**.

If you know someone over the age of 85 then there's a 50/50 chance they are suffering from dementia. Empathy is one of our greatest human traits and gifts. If you can't quite understand how difficult it is for someone with Alzheimer's/Dementia on a daily basis, I would ask that you do these three exercises and then write down how you felt. Understanding where they are helps you meet them where they are and reduce stress for everyone. Emotional understanding is just as, if not more, important than a physically supportive space. When you have both, it's a winning combination for everyone.

**Exercise 1:**

Take a piece of paper and write your name and birth date with your *non-dominant* hand. Now write how this made you feel.

Every day a person with Alzheimer's/Dementia feels this way. They know they were better, yet somehow now slower and disconnected, frustrated, and sometimes it's difficult to even get your brain around how to form the letters. It takes extreme effort and concentration, and yet you've been doing this for years! Imagine 80 years.... You know your name and when you were born, but trying to get it on paper legibly and fast is a task. The brain takes up to 25% of the oxygen needed in your body, which is why mental work is so exhausting.

**Exercise 2:**

Take out a piece of paper and write down all you did in 30-minute increments 2 days ago......from the time you got up till when you went to sleep. Most people don't get very far. Write down how this makes you feel. Now, remember how we snicker when grandma can't remember if she took her pills today or ate breakfast. The more someone sleeps, the more difficult remembering becomes.

**Exercise 3:**

Place your index finger pointed at the sky above your nose (with your head looking up) now turn your finger slowly clockwise, while slowly moving it down (yet close to your body) till it's at your nose and then lower it continuing to turn it clockwise..... now your head should be looking down at your finger and what do you notice? If you have done the exercise correctly your finger has switched to counterclockwise. Magic? Confused? I bet you are; most people will do this 2-3 times before they believe it.

I have a video I created that may help you understand this exercise a little better that you can view on YouTube.

The link is:

**https://www.youtube.com/watch?v=wu7nozJbbY8**

Write down how this made you feel.

What happened? Your perspective changed. My grandmother experiences the world differently than I do because her perspective is different due to the dementia. All the explaining to her in the world can't make her understand my finger was going clockwise if she's looking down on the finger and I am looking up on the finger.

What if every day or hour or minute your perspective changed and disoriented you to understanding your reality? Seems pretty cruel, and then you have people that you thought you were safe with and that loved you arguing with you and you know you're right but they tell you you're not. So you become a bit untrusting and paranoid, they are crazy, not you, right? This happens with my grandma taking her pills, she believes that she has taken them and her perspective says she's 100% right so why would someone force her to take more unless they were trying to hurt her.

This simple exercise can help caregivers, spouses, and family members to understand the change in perspective of someone like my grandmother with Alzheimer's/ Dementia and adapt to using positive manipulation techniques to help get through the normal functions of life vs. arguing with their loved one.

**Exercise 4:**

This exercise comes from Z-Health. You will need 2 people for this exercise and a cell phone to video.

Blindfold yourself and have the other person video you. If possible, place earbuds or ear protection in your ears to help reduce sound.

Now march in place for a minute.

Take off the blindfold and take out the earbuds (if you had them) and see where you are standing now...What happened? When we take away our sight and lose some of our hearing, it is often more difficult than one would expect to understand where we are in this world and that we are moving, even when we think we are staying in one place.

Recognize that aging adults have lost a substantial amount of their senses, from sight to hearing, touch and on.

The largest lesson from these exercises is to have

empathy so that we can meet them where they are. When we come from a place of understanding others and their challenges, communication and connection are increased, which is in direct correlation to having a wonderful quality of life.

Looking back at all I've written I realize I probably come across as some kind of a Worst Case Scenario extremist who has a bunker in her backyard filled to the gills with supplies for an inevitable demise of the human race...but that's not me at all. I'm an optimist at heart, and I think that heart can relax, open up and give Grandma so much more love when my brain's not worrying about what might happen next. The key is to make the space easy for her to use, which means the rest of the family does not need to worry with all the "What If" scenarios.

**The Bathroom do's and don'ts**
**Do's**

- Have the toilet in view of the bed.
- Have an amber night light over the toilet or by the toilet if possible.
- Have a pocket door to the bathroom to allow the entry to be as wide as possible, and ensure at night the door is left open so they can see into the bathroom.
- Have a walk in shower with a seat that is easy to use.
- Have a heat lamp. Core body temperatures of

seniors are lower so when they get out of the shower it's harder for them to get the "chill" off without the heat lamp.

- Have contrasting color towels so they can be seen easily. A different color than the wall works well.
- Have basic needs such as toothpaste and a toothbrush out and accessible.
- Use the safety latches on cabinets to secure what you want kept safe.
- Provide a trash can in an easy to see and reach space.
- Have a bidet toilet seat for ease of personal cleaning.
- Have a contrasting toilet seat for visual cueing.

## Don'ts

- Don't have items available that could cause an issue such as cleaning supplies, mouthwash, etc.
- Don't have medications easily accessible.
- Don't have trip hazards such as rugs.
- Don't have sharp edges, if at all possible.
- Don't have a faucet with 2 blades for water (they may only use the hot or the cold.)
- Don't have carpet as it is difficult to clean if there is an accident, which is more likely closer to the toilet.
- Don't have slippery floors.
- If you have hard floors – avoid tile if possible (vinyl is fine). Grout is difficult to clean and tile is harder if

there is a fall, and so it can cause more damage to the body.

- Don't have curling irons, hair dryers, etc. accessible.
- Don't have an open drain – change it out so that jewelry, etc. doesn't fall in and get lost.
- Don't use a glass cup for water. Use plastic or small disposables.

# 13. Unique Housing Options for Boomers

As we age, our needs change. Kids move out and then maybe back in again and then hopefully out again. Many of us go from an apartment to small houses as we start out in life, to bigger and bigger homes and then we do it all in reverse and downsize. 25 years ago, there were few options as we age, you could downsize to a smaller home or apartment, move to a sunshine state or move in with your family or into senior living.

Now there are so many choices it has become overwhelming and hard to sift through the options, costs and what might work best for us.

To help us decide we need to go back to the foundational questions:

1. How are you going to be able to live your life with freedom and confidence?

2. Will you be living your life?

3. How are you going to care for your mind, body, and spirit?

Sifting through all the different options is difficult but these questions will help you to make smart choices that will offer you freedom, flexibility, and confidence.

To be clear there is no **Right or Wrong** solution. The right solution for you may be the wrong solution for me.

There are options for all different types of unique housing situations, but to be clear, I love senior living, heck it's my life's work! Whenever my husband, my kids and I would tour a new senior living home that my team and I had just designed, we all agreed: we would love to move in. What's not to love? The apartment would be cleaned for us, the laundry done, food prepared for us whenever we wanted, a workout center and the kids would be safe and sound with 100 grandparents around whenever I'm traveling. It seemed to me for a working, traveling mother, senior living was the perfect fit, but the rub was, I just was not old enough......then.

So why shouldn't everyone choose to age in a private pay (resort style) senior living?

Stick with me on this...... because private pay senior living is a lot like sushi!

So that we are on the same page, I am defining private pay as a homes/facilities that do not take Medicaid, basically, it's out of pocket or paid for by your own long-term care insurance policy. Now that we have gotten this out of the way...

Sushi is one of those foods that you either love or hate... sushi is expensive no matter if it's good or great. If you don't like sushi (raw fish), then don't try to make yourself like it, just eat a hamburger (or veggie burger) and do what works for you.

No matter the cost, if you don't like sushi, it's not going to start tasting better to you.

If on the other hand, you like sushi, then go all in. You can try all the variations of how it's made and different types of fish.

I find this analogy to hold true with so many of the beautiful resort style senior living homes we design at Mosaic. Some residents thrive and come back to life when they move into senior living. They love having a community, activities, help and the safety of the environment. Senior Living has reconnected them to life.

On the other hand, my parents want to be in their own home and they want to be by their kids, close, really close (remember they live with us), connection is not an issue for them. So to move them into a senior living would actually cause them disconnection, not greater connection.

It's a matter of taste, do you like sushi or not? As my Italian grandmother would say, "to each his own." In other words, your sushi is fine for you, but not for me.

If you don't have kids or they are grown and you're tired of tending to the yard and doing constant home upkeep, why not look at some interesting alternative ways to live? For instance, did you know that you can actually live aboard a cruise ship and that the cost is comparable to an assisted living facility? How about getting a place together with several of your friends and having a girls' night, every night? Have you considered life as an expatriate in a tropical paradise? You will be surprised to find out how affordable and stress-free that type of life can be! Do your homework and keep your mind open to possibilities that you've never considered before. As the young folks say, you only live once!

While there are so many options, I will do my best to introduce these concepts to you in a simple concise format, it's up to you to decide what piques your interest and then dive in and learn more, applying the 3 foundational questions to help you decide what is best for you.

While traveling to Israel this past summer, I was exposed to something called a Kibbutz concept. It's a community centered around a common goal like agriculture where folks all live together and share resources and duties.

Some would say Israel would not be where it is today if not for these communities. In their Kibbutz living, they have found a unique housing solution that has worked for over a hundred years and is still working. Now, Baby Boomers in the US are applying some of these principles to help improve their quality of life as they age and live on their own terms.

## Co-Housing

Similar to the Israeli Kibbutz housing but you have your own "owned" private spaces and you come together in shared community spaces such as large dining and large gathering spaces. It's similar to assisted living without any services. Neighbors also share resources like tools etc. typically co-housing situations involve 20-40 homes. http://www.cohousing.org/what_is_cohousing

## House Sharing / Endless Girls' (or Boys') Nights

Another alternative that people don't often think of is sharing a home with some friends, *Golden Girls* style. A recent UCLA study points out that one in three baby boomers is unmarried, making this a growing trend. If you never married or are divorced or widowed with several friends in the same situation – why not move in together? It will afford you companionship, fun, and assistance when needed. If one of you has a home that is conducive to home sharing, the others can simply pay rent. Or, you can each sell your homes and possessions and find something that suits all of your lives perfectly. A large condo near the beach, perhaps? Let someone else do all the yard work and keep the pool sparkling. Your only job will be deciding what's for breakfast and how long to stay in the sun.

Don't have any suitable housemates? Check into senior home share programs to find some. The obvious benefit of this type of arrangement is the lowered cost for each participant and companionship.

There's really no right or wrong way to do this, the key is being clear on the rules of engagement from the onset and then having a process in place to deal with them, when or if it goes awry. You know what I mean...When Blanche stays out all night and forgets to call, so the others don't worry ?

## Housing co-ops

These are member owned and run the gamut from apartments to single family homes. You'll find them in specific communities and even mobile home parks. These are less expensive than private pay senior living, have less services but align you with people with the same needs.

## NORC (Naturally Occurring Retirement Community)

NORC's are multigenerational planned neighborhoods that have organized volunteer programs. These neighborhoods provide the structure to allow support services to be in place for all generations in a free volunteer format. **http://ghdc.generationsofhope.org/ initiatives/**

## Niche Retirement

Similar to a CCRC (Continuing Care Retirement Community) but around a niche such as golf, religion, sexual orientation or occupation. These are popping up all over and can allow you to age with your tribe.

## Village to Village

Neighbor helping neighbor with some paid help and organized events. The Village to Village Network was formed in 2010. Currently, there are over 200 of these villages and another 150 coming online in 45 states. They are similar to a NORC, but are created to support aging in place and support reciprocity. Some volunteer service includes wellness programs and transportation. Per their site "VtVN energizes Villages, hyper-local neighborhood groups, of vibrant members engaged in their communities. Village members experience reduced isolation, increased independence, and enhanced purpose of life. These feet on the street resources, focused on social determinants of health, positively improve population health."
http://www.vtvnetwork.org/

## Elder Cottage Housing Opportunities ECHOs / Grand Pods or Flats / Micro Living

These are trailer homes that are attached to existing homes and removed when no longer needed.

You may not want to live like my family does in a multi-generational household, but you also may want to be close, really close to your family without having to share the kitchen or be able to hear and see each other. A new option is the Grand Pod. Think of it like a small cottage placed in the backyard of your daughters or sons home. You have complete privacy, but also have security and can see the family whenever you want without getting into a car or plane. Several companies are making these backyard mini houses, and some have even worked through local permitting with the cities. They range in size from 140 square feet on up. Typically, they are one story. The cost ranges from $85,000 – $250,000. These Grand Pods can be as disconnected or as connected as you want them to be, some even sharing a patio, cover walkways or garage.

MEDCottage is one of the few manufacturers of Grand Pods that have built-in features to age in place such as grab bars, night lights, and emergency call systems. Per their website "The MEDcottage is a mobile medical dwelling designed to be temporarily placed on a caregivers property for rehabilitation and extended care."

The cottage is delivered fully assembled and costs about $60 per day which is very economical considering the options and is a rented model.

One of the great features of the Grand Pod, is that if you decide to not use it in a micro living capacity, it can become a great art studio, workout studio, home office or anything else you can imagine.

**Cruising Through Life**

Amazingly, life on a cruise ship is a great way to travel while taking advantage of amenities quite similar to those of an assisted living facility (ALF). Nearly all cruise ships offer all-inclusive plans that include meals, and there any many entertainment and exercise opportunities. Swimming pools and well-equipped fitness rooms are a fixture of most cruises, live music, shows, and games, and each has onboard doctors.

Cruising costs are typically lower than what you'd pay in a private pay assisted living facility. Consider that the average cost of assisted living is about $3,750 per month, though the costs vary widely by state. Cruises average less than $100 per night. Longer cruises offer even larger discounts, and often a couple's discount can be offered for two people traveling together. There are also senior discounts, discounts for frequent cruisers, and points that you can stack up on a credit card. Be sure to check with the cruise line to see if they allow long-term passengers, or sign up for an around the world voyage that lasts several months. For even more travel variety, you can try different cruises from the same departure point that travel to varied ports of call.

## Road Tripping

Love to get in the car and just drive? Did you ever consider making that your new retirement lifestyle? If nothing is holding you in the town where you live, why not get out the maps and plot your journey? The great thing about road trips is that they can be different things to different people. If you love camping, buying an RV and making friends in campgrounds around the country might be to your liking. Alternatively, if you enjoy creature comforts and hate bugs, driving your luxury SUV to well-appointed hotels around the country might work best. Either way, you can stop to see the sights on your journey that you've always wanted to visit. Better yet, the costs will most likely be less than living in a traditional assisted living facility.

## House Swapping

Have you always wondered what it would be like to live in a certain state or a particular town, or even overseas? House swapping for baby boomers gives you lots of options. After all, there is likely someone out there interested in finding out what living in your area is like, but not as a tourist. Swapping homes gives you the opportunity to stay where you want with limited or no added costs. Of course, most baby boomers are empty nesters with lots of flexibility, making it easier to work out exchanges. Some sites to look into for home exchange:

https://www.homeexchange.com/

https://www.sabbaticalhomes.com/

and https://homeexchange50plus.com/

**Moving to Paradise**

Aside from just visiting somewhere tropical or amazingly historical, you might decide you'd love to live there. Growing numbers of American Boomers are now opting to relocate outside of the United States, to great tropical areas like the Bahamas, coastal Mexico, Belize, and Costa Rica. There are also large numbers of expatriates in countries like Germany, Japan, and the United Kingdom. Most seniors cite the cost of living in these countries as one of their biggest considerations before making a move, with rent and utilities averaging less. Additionally, many boomers find that hiring help in some areas is quite affordable, allowing them to relax and let someone else do the cooking, cleaning, and laundry. Of course, you can't overlook the amazing scenery and culture in many of the places that are burgeoning with expats, as well as the wealth of activities available.

With all of the options now available, look at which strike your fancy before deciding on moving to an independent or assisted living facility. You just might find that you'd prefer laying on a beach under swaying palms!

## Understanding Traditional Aging Housing Options

### CCRC

CCRC is a Continuing Care Retirement Community. Typically you pay a large fee, anywhere from $100,000 to a million dollars and buy into a community that has patio homes, independent living, assisted living, skilled nursing, and memory care. You lock into the monthly rates the year you buy and can move throughout the system as you need. This is a great system for those planners that saved lots of money but sometimes the community can wear down 10 years into your stay. They are offering less flexibility to leave due to your large investment.

### Independent Living

Apartments that are age restricted, typically 55 and older and may have dining facilities, activities and some cleaning services. You can typically get a home health service that is not provided by the community to come in and help with medications and health needs. Costs ranging from $1,500 a month to $20,000 a month depending on the campus, design, location, and services.

## Assisted Living

Apartments that are smaller that Independent Living and have much smaller kitchens, that are not usually equipped with a stove or oven. They are age friendly and attach to lots of services that are part of the monthly rent cost such as (dining, activities, game room, cafe, transportation/van for rides to the doctors office) they also offer a 24/7 nurse on site in most states and assistance with ADL's (assistance with daily living activities such as: bathing, toileting, medications and dressing), these may be over and above your monthly rent or included as a flat fee. These communities are typically a rental program

## Memory Care

Purpose built Memory Care homes have staff that is trained specifically to deal with cognitive issues or memory loss. This could be any form of dementia, which is the umbrella term for anything from Alzheimer's to vascular dementia or Lewy Body disease. Typically, they will have an interior courtyard so that the resident can wander outside without getting into trouble and they utilize technology such as induction cooktops, trackers, circadian lighting and others to help a resident with memory issues have as much freedom as possible while being safe. Costs range from $4500 a month on the low end to $20,000 a month depending on the home. Newer concepts are surfacing where early diagnosis and corrective actions are taken with diet, exercise, and supplements to stop or reverse the disease if caught early enough.

## Skilled Nursing and Short Term Rehabilitation

Skilled nursing typically arises due to a hospital stay or surgery. Stays may be long term or short term. Usually, insurance is involved in this option as this is really a healthcare situation. It's not a choice but a need.

## The Biggest Question I get Asked?

I often get asked, *"If you were moving into AL (Assisted Living), which is the best 'home' you'd choose?"* *"What would you look for, if you had to decide on an AL?"*

So if it's for you, your spouse, or someone else you love, my advice is to look for which providers will give you the most choices, which equals flexibility and freedom.

The kinds of choices that will give you the freedom to live on your terms: mind, body and spirit. Because some private pay assisted living places do—and some do not. There are many AL homes where its a lot like the song Hotel California.... you can check in but you can never check out. They watch your every move and make you sign in and out and track all your guests and their times they come and go. Some even make you sign in and out the key to use the bathroom in the lobby, just like when you were in high school!

For me, I would look for an Independent Living or Assisted Living that will be able to customize things to you. They should give you a suite of options when you move in.

It's actually a lot like a menu and if you want to choose the right restaurant, you need to know what you want (type of food) before you go. Right now the menu for many senior living places is like a restaurant that offers appetizer, entrée and dessert. You *may* be able to find a star rating on it for service, and you *may* be able to find the little dollar signs on it for affordability, but that's about it... that's about the amount of information out there in regards to senior living options. Talk to people and do the research.

In choosing an AL I'd want MORE, than basic living services and a pretty living room. More information that tells me what they're offering in terms of the technology that will help me have the freedom to live on my own terms. What I mean by technology is not just Wifi but also fitness, data mining, robots, IOT, lighting and Well building—all of it!

My final bit of advice is to get clear on what you want using the 3 foundational questions listed in every chapter, then do your research and interview them all.

This is a decision that will impact the rest of your life, even if you're not the one living there.

Clarity creates confidence and confidence creates freedom...

I have provided a simple checklist that will let you ask the right questions if and when you make the decision to move into senior living in the resource section in the back of the book.

# 14. Gamification, Augmented Reality (AR)/Virtual Reality (VR) & Lifelong Learning

You probably would never guess it but, AARP has one of the highest rankings for online games on Google. Playing games and competing against others is fun and healthy, especially when you add exercise. Fitbit and Wii fit are fantastic examples of how games can help you to stay active without having to go into a home and sit in a large room while someone yells BINGO or tosses a balloon around!

Gamification is the process of applying games to tasks to encourage compliance or fun in doing an activity. You're already familiar with gamification if you or anyone you know has ever used Wii Fit. Basically, you are playing a game while exercising, which allows you to focus on the fun or the competition vs. the actual workout.

Another example of gamification that you may not be aware of is fantasy football, which is a multibillion-dollar-a-year industry. The NFL noticed that viewers were not tuning in as much as they used to (probably due to the enormous amount of access to entertainment anytime, anywhere).

Per Wikipedia: "In 1997, **CBS** launched the beta version of the first publicly available free fantasy football website. The game immediately became widely popular. Today, it is estimated that over 19 million people compete in public and private leagues online nationally."

Engagement is key. How do you get your parent or spouse involved and motivated? These are two of the keys to happiness and health. Games seem to be the **Holy Grail** of engagement, but not just any games like solitaire or working a puzzle. Games need to be highly interactive, flexible and ever-changing; this is where gamification comes in. People want to not only immerse themselves in a game but also compete and get rewarded. I may be known to be competitive (blame it on me having two older brothers) but let's be honest, who would rather lose than win?

Why is this important to you? "You can't teach an old dog new tricks" was a saying I was brought up on and implied that once we become mature, the learning stops. We are forever cemented to be who we are and our ability to learn becomes very difficult. To further this sad idea, we were taught up until 2005 that if something catastrophic happened to one part of your brain (such as a stroke), that part was basically dead and could not be recovered. In other words, when your memory starts to go, the old school thinking was that you could never get back what you had lost and it would only get worse over time.

However, in 2005 a study was released that found that when medical students were studied during a period of studying for their exams, their gray matter (the stuff that processes information in your brain) actually increased. This then became known as a mainstream concept called neuroplasticity.

The concept, simplified, is that if you exercise your brain, you can keep it healthy just as you would if you exercise your body, and doing so also deters the effects of aging and possibly even reverse them. Several doctors and futurists have written books on this concept and numerous companies are cashing in on "brain games." A lot of Boomers are adopting this mindset. They fear they will end up like their senile parents or grandparents, and if that's not reason enough, it's because to them it just makes good sense. The word "senile" is hardly used any longer, but it refers to a person having or showing weaknesses or diseases of old age, especially a loss of mental faculties. Now doctors are more specific with their diagnoses such as Alzheimer's and Dementia.

Lumosity is for athletes, it's for kids, it's for seniors, it's for Boomers, and it's for you and me. It's a phone app that utilizes gamification to improve your memory, increase focus and find calm. Elevate, which I actually play, is a free app and it does the same thing as Lumosity, essentially. Brain Fit Life is software that not only helps your brain to stay fit by playing games, but it also provides support and creates a brain report.

"We are NOT just playing games with your brain"
– Dr. Daniel Amen

A COMPREHENSIVE BRAIN HEALTH PROGRAM LIKE NO OTHER.

| RESULTS | Lumosity | CogniFit | Br. Brains | BrainFit Life |
|---|---|---|---|---|
| Brain Type Report | | | | ✓ |
| Memory & Attention | ✓ | ✓ | ✓ | ✓ |
| Stress & More! | | | | ✓ |
| Monitors Progress | ✓ | ✓ | ✓ | ✓ |
| Personalized Meal & Fitness Plans | | | | ✓ |
| Nutritional Tips | | | | ✓ |
| Family Doctor Resources | | | | ✓ |
| Medication Resources | | | | ✓ |
| Community Support | | | | ✓ |
| Club Webinars & Online Coaching | | | | ✓ |

Dr. Daniel Amen, one of the leading psychiatrists on brain health, speaks about the fact that psychiatry is the only medical field that guesses to diagnose instead of using the technology we have today in imaging and blood work than any other doctor would use to help them create a proper diagnosis so that they can create the most successful treatment strategy. According to Dr. Mehmet Oz, "Dr. Amen is one of the most gifted minds in medicine."

He uses the example of Abraham Lincoln being diagnosed as depressed based upon his symptoms of being depressed. The astonishing fact is that this was 173 years ago and the way diagnosis is made today by most doctors is the same as it was then.

While Dr. Amen has been at the forefront of NFL concussion research and debate and helping to heal players from traumatic brain injuries, he is concerned about all brain health and has written books not only on ADD/ADHD but also aging, including *Use Your Brain to Change Your Age: Secrets to Look, Feel, and Think Younger Every Day*. Dr. Amen's latest book *Memory Rescue* is a must read if you want to maintain your memory. He gives simple, actionable plans (with research to back it up) to keep your mind sharp through reducing sugar and increasing physical and mental exercises.

The relevance to anyone 45 years old and older is that Alzheimer's and dementia in mostly diagnosed by symptoms. Rarely is a brain scan completed or labs taken to determine if there is another cause for the memory loss. It's just as rare for those scans and labs to be used to see whether memory loss could be reversed through supplements and/or medication, TMS, psychological testing, neurofeedback, lifestyle changes, bioidentical hormone replacement therapy, oxygen therapy, hypnotherapy, IV nutrient therapy, prolotherapy or platelet-rich plasma therapy. Not all of these therapies are for memory loss – some are for depression, anxiety, joint aches, etc.

As I mentioned in chapter 9, if you're in your 70s and you start to have memory loss, you're written off from really finding out what the issue is and if there's a possibility you could be "fixed" back to a higher level of cognitive function. SPECT scans that look at brain blood flow and activity patterns have been shown to change the treatment plan or diagnosis 78.9 percent of the time vs. just asking the patient for their symptoms. This translates to almost 8 out of 10 treatment plans being wrong when not using the technology that we currently have at our disposal. I know this sounds crazy but it's true. Why would you ever accept a brain diagnosis that is going to rob you of your memories and loved ones without having a brain scan first?

If you're anything like me, I don't always feel like my mind is as quick as it was in my 20's. Maybe it's because I am less active, maybe it's because my cells are dying and have become senescent, or maybe I am developing a form of dementia.... The thought goes through my mind, and frankly, it worries me.

Keeping your brain fit and even turning back the clock to when you felt like you were firing on all cylinders, thinking clearer and faster is the goal of brain exercises through gamification. Dr. Amen has a brain type assessment that you take online and then they direct you to brian exercises and even diet to help you your risk of Alzheimer's disease and stay at your best you, mentally.

*"There is a fountain of youth: it is your mind, your talents, the creativity you bring to your life and the lives of people you love. When you learn to tap this source, you will truly have defeated age." ~Sophia Loren*

An excellent example of the power of gamification is Volkswagen's Fun Theory. They are a group that sets out to change behaviors by utilizing fun or gamification. They have completed numerous experiments with throwing trash away, taking the stairs vs. the escalator, and even reducing speeding in your car. If you have flown lately on Delta Airlines, you would have noticed that their safety video is actually fun and it helps you to pay attention. While we can't make everything fun, there is a lot more we can do to positively manipulate behavior to get the desired results we want, all while having fun. If you have children or have ever babysat, you know how to play this game ... from potty training, to making the food on a spoon become an airplane or train with actual sound effects for the mouth to open and the food to go in, this is the basic concept of gamification.

Don't get me wrong; I am not implying that we should treat others as toddlers. What I am saying is, that if a process must be completed, such as exercising or taking medications, why can't we make it a little fun, or gamify the process? We can build in rewards to encourage the outcomes we want so that it becomes a win-win, something that is not only fun but challenging and gets us excited. This one technology, if applied properly, could dramatically improve the results in almost every aspect of what you do. This is not exactly brain surgery, but it could actually save your brain!

The Fun Theory site states, "This site is dedicated to the thought that something as simple as fun is the easiest way to change people's behavior for the better. Be it for yourself, for the environment, or for something entirely different, the only thing that matters is that it's a change for the better." They encourage participation by offering a fun theory award and testing the top winner's theories.

Some of Volkswagen's Fun Theory experiments in how to manipulate behavior for the better and have fun are eye-opening to say the least, and I would highly encourage you to watch the videos and brainstorm how you may engage the concept in your life.

The most famous of the experiments involves a piano staircase, in which folks are encouraged to take the staircase vs. the escalator out of the subway. They recorded data with cameras of how many individuals took the stairs vs. the escalators and then came in and installed a weight-activated piano on the staircase like the one in the Tom Hanks movie *Big*. Sound would come out as people stepped on the keys of the stairs. Some would try to play a song on the way up and out of the subway while others tried to hold back a smile. The end result was there was a 66 percent increase in people taking the stairs vs. the escalator!

Another example of the Fun Theory was "The World's Deepest Bin." They took a trash can in a park and rigged a motion sensor sound to it so that when trash was thrown into the bin or can, it made a sound like it never hit the bottom. People would actually go looking for more trash on the ground to throw into the bin just to hear the sound again or to try and figure it out. In the end, 158 lbs. were collected in the trash bin in one day, which was 90 lbs. more than the next-closest bin.

The final Fun Theory example was through a contest for Fun Theory ideas. The contest winner postulated that you could reduce speeding by entering those obeying the speed limit into a lottery to win some of money gained by those who were speeding and issued tickets. The concept was simple: get more people to obey the speed limit by giving them a chance to win money from those that broke the law. The results were not surprising: speeding was reduced by 22 percent. Apparently, positive reinforcement works better than negative.

Given the results, it seems ridiculous not to employ more of the Fun Theory in our lives. Who would not want a 66 percent positive increase in participation of any item that we already do? Imagine what this could do to increase your quality of life.

## Augmented Reality and Virtual Reality

Take a moment to think about all the technologies that you use today that you did not have when you were a kid. One technology that comes to mind is the cellular phone. Take this one step further to the smartphone. It can not only call others, but you can text, look up anything on the internet, have it remind you of appointments and help you get to a location when your driving. It's incredible what a smartphone can do today.

I was recently challenged to fast from my smartphone and computer/tablet from Saturday night till Monday morning. Easy peasy right? Not really, I had no idea how much I rely on my electronics. Both my kids are in college so they can find for themselves yet I was making up excuses in my mind of why I needed to keep my phone on in case they needed me and texted me. When I was in college, I had a phone in my apartment with no answering machine and if I was not at home when my parents called then they could not get ahold of me and vice versa. I know you understand this but for the millennials reading this book I felt the need to explain, LOL.

Technology has become part of me, and while I could not have imagined when I was young that in the future I would sleep with my phone, have to turn the car around and go back home if I forgot my phone, and rely on it for my access to the world, my money and memories (all my photos). I can tell you that Augmented Reality and Virtual Reality are going to change how we live and they will help us much in the same way that our smartphones do today but at a multiple of 10 times!

So what is Augmented Reality (AR) and Virtual Reality (VR)?

If you have ever watched Monday night football on TV, AR is the line that is superimposed on the field to show you where first down should be. If you have not watched Monday night football, maybe you have used your smartphone or tablet to go on a furniture or paint site such as Sherwin Williams. If you take a photo of your living room you can change the paint color on the screen to see how it will look before you buy the paint and paint the entire room! Pretty cool technology right.

VR is more immersive, it's like playing a video game but you are inside the game. If you are unfamiliar with video games the best analogy I can give you is being in a 3-D movie theatre. You have special glasses on and the room is dark and you feel like your're in the movie.

**AUGMENTED REALITY (AR)**

Think of Augmented Reality (AR) as your "life GPS."

Here's what I mean: AR mixes your current reality with your "virtual reality."

Think about what happens when you're using your GPS; it's reading your current reality on the actual street you're driving on and, at the same time, it's also telling you where to go—which is your virtual reality—you're not actually there, it's where you'll be in the near future (traffic problems notwithstanding!) And it's doing it in a way that takes the stress out of driving because it's clear, it's straightforward and it's not emotional. It's not like the days when you had to pull over and unfold a complicated map, or, the passenger had to use the map and direct you; those were the days of emotional navigation!

**How AR might show up in your life:**

One of the ways people envision AR to show up in your life is that you would have glasses that you use to see but also for added information AR information such as GPS, this way you don't have to look down at your phone or GPS on your car. Advertisers are looking to leverage this technology by automatically popping up advertisements as your walking down the street or through the mall. Imagine you're shopping and advertisers suddenly jump into your world: walking past a Victoria Secret and you get an ad in front of your glasses that says, Buy 2 pair of underpants and get 1 free, or walking passed Golf Galaxy and there's a sale on the driver you've been wanting.

Another use for AR is being able to turn any surface into a game board. Just like when you're watching an NFL game and they overlay the 1st down line on the field, your glasses would overlay a game onto a surface. Instead of playing solitaire on my phone, I could play it on my coffee table or TV tray.

One of the more exciting applications for AR glasses is for travelers. Imaging being in Pompeii, Italy and looking at the ruins. Your AR glasses show you what the areas looked like prior to the volcanic eruption! They give you facts and details that make the experience so much richer, augmenting the experience without the annoying struggle of hearing the tour guide.

AR is already available on your smartphone and you may be using it. IKEA has an Augmented Reality app that you can use on your tablet or phone. This app allows you to see their furniture in your home without having to buy a thing! This way you can make decisions without having to buy something and then possibly return it. Basically, your camera shows the room and then you drag furniture items from the menu into the camera view and it "augments" the space to show you what it will look like with that piece of furniture in it, pretty neat!

Currently, most of the glasses are either still in development, used for business or are being made for drone users, cyclists or as sunglasses.

Some of the following products may be of interest to you if you.

- **AR Apps for your Phone**
  - **Google Sky Map** – This AR App lets you look at the sky and it will point out constellations, planets, and stars.
  - **Pokemon Go** – If you have grandkids you might already know about this AR game. Basically, you have the app open on your phone and when your phone vibrates you will see a Pokemon (cartoon character that will look like it's on the street, etc where your camera on your phone is looking and you throw a virtual ball at it to get points). The game is so popular it's been downloaded over 750 million times
  - **Google Translate** – This is a great one for Boomer Travelers. Basically, hold your camera phone so that it can see a sign in another language or menu and it will be translated on your phone immediately through AR. Super cool, easy to use and helpful!
  - **Google Goggles** – Point your phone's camera at something and it will read it and tell you something, having a "discussion" with a loved one over who painted that painting? Just use Google's Goggles and the mystery will be solved. it can also read QR codes which can link you to

other information.

- ○ **IKEA Place** – A Swedish furniture company has created an AR where you can try furniture prior to buying. You access the app and aim your camera looking at the room you wish in your home and then drag furniture pieces you like into the room and magically a chair looks like it is sitting in your living room! A must for anyone downsizing. Even if you do not want IKEA furniture ( the seat heights are a bit lower than desired for Boomers) you can get an idea of what works and fits in your new space.

- ○ **Sherwin Williams Visualizer** – This tool helps you to see what your paint color looks like on your walls prior to all the cost and work of painting. Just upload a photo of your room to the visualizer and select a paint, and voila! the room changes color, don't like it, just tap and choose a new color. Great tool if you want to freshen up where you live, get ready to sell or if you just bought a new place.

- **Own a business that requires a lot of training or 3-D Communication:**

- ○ **Microsoft HoloLens** – As an interior designer, this technology is very cool, basically I could walk into a home and place furniture from a catalog into the space and rearrange it until I get the look I want. This is similar to the IKEA Place but can be anything I want and can also collaborate with others through the glasses. Onsite technicians such as an elevator repair guy can wear the glasses and the home office can see what he is seeing immediately and help him with support and even tutorials, saving time and increasing safety.

- **Google Glass** – These have been around since 2013 but Google pulled back and now is only selling them as an enterprise edition. While they look kinda like glasses, they really are just a very small screen attached to the frame of glasses that give information. Boeing and medical doctors are testing them now. I am not sure of the relevance to Boomers but thought inquiring minds would want to know their status as they were the first ones on the scene.

- **Magic Leap** – Technically they are developing for both business (enterprise) and consumers (you and me). The only version available at this time of writing is the Leap one, it costs about $2,200 and is meant for developers. I had the pleasure of trying out the headset and found it comfortable and easy to use. Not sure how long you could wear them comfortably but they do seem to work really well.

- **Meta 2** – A similar product to HoloLens. If you

are designing a product this helps you to troubleshoot issues prior to going into production which is a huge win for any designer.

- **Cycle:**
  - **Vara Vision** – This AR device attaches to your sunglasses or glasses and gives you information on approaching cars, your personal performance data, and directions.
  - **Solos** – These sunglasses have built-in AR to give you data like that of Vara Vision and also your health metrics. It will also give you phone call notifications and allow you to stay connected while you keep your eyes on the road.
  - **Raptor** – These sunglasses are for those that want to stay connected, know their sats, take video and photos and share and keep their eyes on the road.

- **Out in the sun quite a bit:**
  - **Vuzix Blade AR** – These sunglasses mirror whatever is on your smartphone so you can keep up with all the incoming emails and facebook posts.

- **Fly Drones:**

- **Epson Moverio BT-300FPV Drone Edition** – I don't fly drones but we have one, these AR glasses allow you to see the controls while you are watching the drone fly vs. looking down at the controls then back up again, then back down....well you get the point. The experience is much more user-friendly and enjoyable.

**How VR might show up in your life:**

Want to learn a new language? Sculpt without the mess? Play a video game in 3-D? Travel to distant lands or underwater? Meditate? Meet new people from around the world or take a tour of an ancient Egyptian tomb all from your living room sofa? Welcome to Virtual Reality.

I have to admit the thought of messing up my hair and putting on a headset where I could not see who was around me, was daunting to say the least. I avoided it for quite a while until I learned all the positive aspects. Then I tried VR at a conference, what I experienced was so immersive that I forgot all about what my hair looked like and who was in the room. It was wonderfully liberating and fun! I was able to connect with people in different countries and felt like we were together. I felt happiness just like it was a real situation. Think of going to the movies and multiply it by 100.

## How VR might show up in your life:

There is a current movie out called Ready Player 1 (highly recommend watching this to understand VR) plus the movie is situated in Columbus, Ohio where I live so I have to promote the city that I love. The concept is that when you live in a not so great environment that Virtual Reality (VR) can help you to escape it to a better virtual reality. This means if you're not able to travel anymore, don't have the funds, your body is not as able as it used to be or your alone and want to experience more than books and TV. Just put on the headset and you're off to do whatever, wherever, with anyone you want.

And it feels real, so real that your brain thinks it's real by the chemicals it produces.

This is not a placebo effect, research was conducted by Tsinghua University and Immersive lab regarding the Qinghua elderly study and their response to VR use. Per Qiyong Chen from Vive Immersive Lab "we measured the elderly's emotional status using SAM (Self-Assessment Manikin) scale before and after they used Vive Pro. Then we compared the data and discover VR can effectively help the elderly to get emotional arousal. We also used a wristband to test EDA (Electro Dermal Activity) and HR (Heart Rate) at the same time, which will help us know if the subjects correctly express their emotional state. In addition, I am looking forward to that if you can do more scene comparison, like walking, growing flowers, etc." It's such exciting research that we are partnering with Vive and Research Square to reproduce this study worldwide.

If you don't want to play games there are many applications that can let you learn, explore, create and meditate. you could tour the tomb of Christ, Paint and sculpt in 3-D with Tilt Brush (I personally have used this and was inspired to paint again.) Explore the sea without getting wet or Mars for that matter. or you could just chill and meditate. The possibilities are endless and incredibly engaging. you are transported to another world while you sit or stand in your bedroom or living room, it's the closest thing to space and time travel. It's liberating for the mind body and spirit and can change your attitude in a second.

When I first started down the path of virtual reality, it was a bit overwhelming. Keep in mind it's a lot like having a car, I don't have to know how the engine works or be able to fix it to drive a car and have fun on a road trip. Virtual Reality Glasses (you need these to use virtual reality games and programs) work with a computer system and typically the internet. Like a TV, you still need to plug it in, have cable or Wi-Fi and then pay for channels for your entertainment. Unlike a TV you can go anywhere and do anything! Think about the massive difference between radio and black and white tv and then color tv. VR takes you INTO the entertainment and allows you to control where you go and what you do. frankly, it's one of the most liberating things I have experienced, and I have driven a Nascar on the Brickyard (Indy 500 track), Hang glided, scuba dived and sculpted. And it's safe ?

First, you will need a gaming computer or PlayStation to use virtual reality. Then you need the glasses. Any big box store can help you with the right computer and your existing one may already work. The important thing to remember is you need to have a graphics card that will work for VR/gaming. The graphics card needs to be more powerful than a regular computer that you would be using for email and Facebook. Basically, VR has more FPS (frames per second) so that you don't get motion sick. Trust me, I get motion sick on boats, cars, and planes but I have been fine when doing VR.

Here's what to look for when you buy a computer:

- Strong Graphics Card
- HDMI video output, typically
- Computer engine has to be fast
- Memory 8GB or higher of RAM (it's like your short term memory)

Please don't get worried about knowing what to get, whoever you buy from can help you out easily. Expect to spend a minimum of $600.00 for the computer.

Some of the following products may be of interest to you if you.

**VR Glasses:**

**Oculus Rift – $399 –** One of the best rated VR glasses out there, very powerful and pretty easy to set up. It is tethered which means that there will be a cord from the headset (glasses) to the computer. Personally, I think being tethered is not a big issue as I would recommend doing VR sitting down to start off with until you get comfortable.

**HTC Vive – $499 –** This powerful VR set has support handled controls and whole room VR. HTC is the leader in research on VR and seniors and has clinical studies showing an improvement of mood while using VR. It is tethered.

**Sony PlayStation VR – $399 –** This powerful VR set works with a PlayStation gaming device vs. a computer. It is still tethered.

**Samsung Gear – $99 –** This powerful VR set works with a PlayStation gaming device vs. a computer. It is still tethered. Samsung Gear- 99 works but difficult to find content

**Oculus Go – $199 –** This VR is standalone, meaning no cord tying you to a computer. It still needs one to work but your movement can be more free, especially when playing games. Facebook acquired Oculus for 2.3 Billion, yes Billion. Oculus Go's low price is intended to get into everyone's home, in other words, VR is the TV of the future.

**HTC Vive Pro – $799 –** Most awesome tethered VR – tracks your movements to the millimeter in real-life movement 360 degrees. Built-in eye tracking.

**Lenovo Mirage Solo with Daydream – $359** This VR is a standalone (non-tethered) VR.

**Google Daydream View – $79** This VR is intended to work with a smartphone such as a Google Pixel or Pixel XL. it's basically goggles that you snap your smartphone. While I have the phone and the goggles, I am concerned about my data package on my phone going through the roof. some of the apps are the Washington post VR and Youtube VR, there are others but very limited.

**R-9 Smartglasses – $1,999 –** While these are on a waiting list for release, they are much smaller than most VR sets and look like a pair of sunglasses. They will also do both AR and VR.

**Rendover –** these VR glasses are made specifically for senior living homes. These operate similar to other VR glasses but the content delivered ( what you can see) is tailored towards seniors. Imagine hiking up Machu Picchu or visiting your favorite park all virtually.

**VR Games & Experiences:** Once you have your glasses you can download various games and experiences. Think of it like this, the VR headset is your record player and downloadable games and experiences are your albums (music). Some will be free and others you will need to pay for. Please note, not all apps work with all glasses.

**the Blu: –** This is a deeply immersive experience that transports you under the sea to a sunken ship. you will see incredible sea life and even a whale. Explore the reef, travel to the bottom of the sea and discover the iridescent sea life or explore a sunken ship.

**Apollo 11 –** Relive the full experience of Neil Armstrong and Buzz Aldrin from inside the cockpit, become an astronaut and take the controls on the greatest journey of mankind.

**Google Earth (FREE) –** Go anywhere you want with this app, you can fly, walk around or easily pick from preloaded locations such as the Giza Pyramids, Rome or Iceland. Choose to stroll the streets of your hometown or watch a solar eclipse.

**Rapid Fire: A Brief History of Flight –** This app transports you to the airstrip of an air show but not any airshow, you will see close up the history of all planes close up.

**Tilt Brush –** Want to paint, sculpt without the mess or

any spatial restrictions? Then Tilt Brush is for you. The first time I tried Tilt Brush, it was one of the most fun, liberating experiences I have ever had. You can zoom in on what you're creating and back out again, if you make a mistake you can easily erase. It's not just for art, you can create anything from a new invention to decorating your house.

**Within (FREE)** – This app has content from around the world, from NBC, the New York Times, to watching a dance video or concert.

**FirstHand Technology** – While this VR experience is not available to the general public. Opiates used to treat pain have been fairly unsuccessful as pain is just a signal to the brain. VR is being used to rewire the brain to reduce and eliminate nerve pain. Basically, playing guided games and activities can help you to regain your life back, pain-free.

AR and VR are here to stay and can help us to stay connected, create, collaborate and explore new worlds through education and entertainment. I would highly recommend getting on board with these technologies. They will be as common in the near future as your computer or smartphone, but much more engaging and liberating.

### Lifelong Learning

While some Boomers are moving back onto their Alma

mater college campus and signing up for one class so that they have full access to all the university has to offer such as the cafeteria, library, fitness facilities and tons of youth to engage with, others are engaging in other ways such as traveling, VR classes or simply listening to podcasts.

Want to give back, share and learn? Check out https://www.lifeguides.com/ This new platform connects people that have experienced an issue, such as aging parents and now have "wisdom" with those that are in need of this wisdom. It's an incredible way to help others and learn more about yourself and the world. This is truly a multi-generational wisdom share.

As I have discussed in previous chapters how house swapping and Airbnb friendly services for seniors can give you the freedom to travel with ease cost effectively, there is also the Evergreen Club which allows you to stay on others homes (like a mini bed and breakfast version) for around 20 dollars a day! Imagine the museums, concerts, classes, and tours you could go on with this kind of savings on your stay. Heck, even if you stay with friends you still obligated to buy them dinner or bring them a gift. https://www.evergreenclub.com/ is probably cheaper than staying with friends and family. Also, check out http://travellingboomer.com/ a blog for boomers that travel.

Want to travel the world, go on an adventure, learn

something new and meet new people? The Road Scholar experience is for you. https://www.roadscholar.org/

Learning does not always have to be on campus or in a physical classroom, Osher Lifelong Living Institute offers many classes to peak your interest, keep your mind sharp and have something to talk about more than the weather or your favorite game show. Other online class portals include:

Online Course Platforms:

- **Udemy – https://www.udemy.com/**
- **Teachable – https://teachable.com/**
- **Ruzuku – https://www.ruzuku.com/**
- **WizIQ – https://www.wiziq.com/**
- **Educadium – https://www.educadium.com/**
- **SkillShare – https://www.skillshare.com/**
- **Coursera – https://www.coursera.org/**

By the time you read this, there will probably be many more. Do your research and find out which ones will be best for what you are interested in.

Another great way to learn is through podcasts.....

What's a podcast? I had the same question a couple of years ago. So, I thought instead of you going through the pain of figuring this out like I had too, we are friends now and friends help each other out, so I wrote you a podcast how to.

What the Heck is a Podcast and why should I be listening to them?

*Podcasts* are free, downloadable audio shows. There are thousands, if not millions of podcasts available. While they've been around for over a decade now, podcasts are seeing a surge of popularity with independent shows like Serial and Radiolab, in addition to podcasts from the likes of ESPN and National Public Radio.

The beauty of listening to a podcast is that you can listen to whatever you want, whenever you want. Imagine, having millions of radios shows on everything from health, sports, cooking, news or entertainment at your fingertips. You don't have to worry about missing your favorite radio talk show or not being able to hear it all when you need to answer someone at the door.

Unlike traditional radio or television, podcasts require a bit of work to set up, but once you're there a world of audio enjoyment awaits. It may seem a bit daunting at first, but once you get started the process becomes second nature.

When it comes to lifelong learning, you can pick which areas you want to learn more about and go as shallow or as deep as you would like with podcasts.

A tool called a *podcatcher* is used to download podcasts. Think of a podcatcher like a TV or radio station where you get to choose all the programming. Most podcasts are available in all podcatchers, so in general, you won't have to worry about missing out on your preferred device.

There are a number of different podcatchers available for Windows computers, Macs, iPhones, iPads, Android phones, Kindle Fire tablets, and even some televisions. Each tool should have a directory included where you can search for podcasts by name, topic, or keyword. Many also come with recommendations or charts to let you know what's popular.

After you've found the podcast you want to listen to, you can subscribe to it (similar to subscribing to a newspaper or newsletter). This will download the most recent episode and make sure that every new episode downloads as well. You can also download individual episodes if you want to check the back catalog, or if you just want one or two episodes before you decide to subscribe. Subscribing costs nothing, and helps the show creators gain visibility, so if you like a show you should subscribe!

Once the podcast you want to hear has downloaded, you can usually click or tap on it to play it back. You can listen to it as many times as you want. Some podcatchers will delete a show after you listen to it, but you can always download episodes again whenever you'd like.

To sum up, the steps to get started with listening to podcasts are as follows:

1. Download a podcatcher
2. Search the directory in that podcatcher to find the show you want to hear
3. Download individual episodes, or subscribe
4. Play your podcast!

Using Apple Podcasts on iPhones and iPads

1. Go to your Apple App Store (unless the podcast is already showing on your device, then skip to step 3).
2. Download and install the Podcasts app from the App Store.
3. Launch the app. You'll be greeted with a welcome screen with some basic info about the app. Tap Start Listening Now to proceed.
4. To search for a podcast, tap the Search icon in the lower-right corner.
5. Tap in the text field under Search and type in whatever you'd like to search for. For example seniors, baby boomers, etc. Then tap the blue Search button in the lower-left corner.
6. The search results will load. Shows will appear at the top, and swiping them to the left will reveal more

results. Individual episodes that match your search term will appear below.

7. Tap on an episode to reveal its details. You can press the Play button to stream the episode, or the + button to add it to your library, then tap the download icon to listen on the go.

8. If you tap on a show in your results, you'll then see the info page for that show, along with recent episodes. You can tap the + on an individual episode to add it to your library, or tap Subscribe to have the app automatically download the most recent episode and all future episodes.

9. You can find unplayed and recently listened to podcasts by tapping the Listen Now icon in the lower-left corner. To see all your subscriptions, tap the Library icon to the right of the Listen Now icon.

Using Podcast Addict on Android

1. Go to the Google Play Store on your phone.

2. Download and install Podcast Addict or other "podcatcher" from the Google Play Store.

3. Launch the app. You'll be greeted with a Get Started screen. To add a podcast, tap the + icon in the upper-right corner.

4. Tap the Search Engine tile in the upper-left corner.

5. Tap the text field and type in whatever you'd like to search for. For example seniors, baby boomers, etc.

Check the box for Use iTunes Search Engine. Then, tap Search.

6. Your search results will load in two tabs: Podcasts and Episodes.

7. To subscribe to a listed podcast, tap the checkmark next to it. This will have the app automatically download the most recent episode and all future episodes.

8. You can also tap the Episodes tab to see episodes that match your search. Tap on the episode's name to stream it, or tap the download button to save it to your device for listening on the go.

# Pod catchers

A comparison chart is a helpful tool in decision making.
In one glance, the features and qualities

WWW.LISAMCINI.COM

| NAME | SYSTEM | STREAMING | DOWNLOAD | PLAYBACK/OFFLINE | AUTO UPDATE | SEARCHABLE | TRENDING FEATURE | COST | PROS | CONS |
|---|---|---|---|---|---|---|---|---|---|---|
| Spotify | 🤖🍎 | ✓ | ✓ | ✓ | ✗ | ✓ | ✓ | | Built into Spotify app. | Ads inserted into audio unless on Spotify Premium plan. No options to subscribe to podcasts. |
| Stitcher Radio for Podcasts | 🤖🍎 | ✓ | ✓ | ✓ | ✓ | ✓ | ✓ | | Customizable playlists. Great for discovery. Exclusive shows. | Ads inserted into audio unless on Stitcher Premium plan. |
| TuneIn Radio | 🤖🍎 | ✓ | ✓ | ✓ | ✓ | ✓ | ✓ | | Upgrade to TuneIn Premium for live play-by-play of NFL, MLB, and Barclays Premier League games, commercial-free music stations, and an audio book library. | Preroll ads unless on TuneIn Premium. Banner ads without Premium or a one time Pro unlock. |
| Podbean | 🤖🍎 | ✓ | ✓ | ✓ | ✓ | ✓ | ✓ | | Also includes an audio recorder. Free. | Discovery might be focused on shows using Podbean hosting, their primary product. |
| Spreaker Podcast Radio | 🤖🍎 | ✓ | ✓ | ✓ | ✓ | ✓ | ✓ | | Free. | No speed adjustments. Similar to Podbean. |
| Pocket Casts | 🤖🍎 | ✓ | ✓ | ✓ | ✓ | ✓ | ✓ | $3.99 | Trim Silence. Volume Boost | Paid app. |
| Podcast Republic | 🤖 | ✓ | ✓ | ✓ | ✓ | ✓ | | | Free with ads. Playlist support. | Ad Supported; can be removed with one-time purchase. |
| Player FM | 🤖 | ✓ | ✓ | ✓ | ✓ | ✓ | | | Free. Optional features via subscription. | Reserves the right to show ads in the future. |
| Podcast Addict | 🤖 | ✓ | ✓ | ✓ | ✓ | ✓ | | | Supports video podcasts, YouTube channels, audiobooks, streaming radio and other media sources. | Ad supported. |
| Beyond Pod | 🤖 | ✓ | ✓ | ✓ | ✓ | ✓ | ✓ | $6.99 | Fine-grain download settings give users control of how much the app downloads in the background. | Paid app. Features are lost after 7 days unless full version is purchased. |
| Dogg Catcher | 🤖 | ✓ | ✓ | ✓ | ✓ | ✓ | ✓ | $2.99 | Plays video as well. Variable speed playback. | Paid app with no trial. |
| AntennaPod | 🤖 | ✓ | ✓ | ✓ | ✓ | ✓ | ✓ | | Variable speed playback. Ability to tip podcasters. Open source application. | Maintained by volunteers. Designed for power users. |
| Google Play Music | 🤖 | ✓ | ✓ | ✓ | ✓ | ✓ | | | Included on most Android devices by default. | Lacks additional features offered by most third-party apps. |
| Apple Podcasts | 🍎 | ✓ | ✓ | ✓ | ✓ | ✓ (Charts) | | | Easy to use. Syncs across iOS devices. | Lacks additional features offered by most third-party apps. |
| Overcast | 🍎 | ✓ | ✓ | ✓ | ✓ | | | | Smartspeed and Voice Boost features. Playlists. Great developer support. Upload your own audio files for later listening with optional patronage. Recommended podcasts from Twitter and the author. | Slightly more complex than Apple Podcasts. |
| Castro | 🍎 | ✓ | ? | ✓ | ✓ | ✓ | ✓ | $3.99 | Triage feature to organize podcasts for playback. | Paid app with no trial. May be difficult to learn Triage. |
| iCatcher! | 🍎 | ✓ | ✓ | ✓ | ✓ | ✓ | ✓ | $2.99 | Gesture support for eyes-free use. | Paid app with no trial. |
| Downcast | 🍎 | ✓ | ✓ | ✓ | ✓ | ✓ | ✓ | $2.99 | Variable speed playback. Gesture support. | Paid app with no trial. |
| RSSRadio | 🍎 | ✓ | ✓ | ✓ | ✓ | ✓ | ✓ | $3.99 (In-app Ads) | Free with ads. Playback speed adjustment. | No list view. Difficult to find search for new podcasts. |

www.LisaMCini.com

Chapter 14 - Gamification, Augmented Reality (AR)/Virtual Reality (VR) & Lifelong Learning | 323

# 15. Pets

As you know by now our family loves animals and they are an integral part of unconditional love, stress relief and keeping active. While our family has had dogs, chickens, and bees, I felt it was critically important to find the best source for you. Luckily, America's Favorite Veterinarian and the #1 Amazon Best-Selling Author, Dr. Gary Richter was kind enough to write this chapter. If you would like to know more information from Dr. Gary Richter please check out his website https://www.drgaryrichter.com/ and books on Amazon.

## Unconditional Love: A Boomer's Guide to Pets – Dr. Gary Richter

Relationships can be complicated. Whether it's marriage, family, or friendship, maintaining healthy relationships with people takes time and effort. Despite the work involved, nurturing connections with those who care for us is one of the things that keeps us healthy and give us purpose. There are times however when what we really need is someone to walk with, talk with, and share affection with in a way no human can offer. There are times when what we need most is the unconditional love only a pet can provide.

In addition to love and affection, did you know that pets

are good for your health? Studies indicate pet ownership can be associated with improved cardiovascular health, lower blood pressure and cholesterol.[1][2]

In addition, owning a pet leads to increases in daily activities and decreases loneliness.[3][4][5] All in all, pets are good for our bodies and our spirits.

1. 1 Arhant-Sudhir, K., Arhant-Sudhir, R., & Sudhir, K. (2011). Pet ownership and cardiovascular risk reduction: Supporting evidence, conflicting data and underlying mechanisms. Clinical and Experimental Pharmacology and Physiology,38(11), 734- 738. doi:10.1111/j.1440-1681.2011.05583.x
2. Schreiner, P. J. (2016). Emerging Cardiovascular Risk Research: Impact of Pets on Cardiovascular Risk Prevention. Current Cardiovascular Risk Reports,10(2). doi:10.1007/s12170-016-0489-2
3. Krause-Parello, C. A. (2012). Pet Ownership and Older Women: The Relationships Among Loneliness, Pet Attachment Support, Human Social Support, and Depressed Mood. Geriatric Nursing,33(3), 194-203. doi:10.1016/j.gerinurse.2011.12.005
4. Raina, P., Waltner-Toews, D., Bonnett, B., Woodward, C., & Abernathy, T. (1999). Influence of Companion Animals on the Physical and Psychological Health of Older People: An Analysis of a One-Year Longitudinal Study. Journal of the American Geriatrics Society,47(3), 323-329. doi:10.1111/j.1532-5415.1999.tb02996.x
5. Pikhartova, J., Bowling, A., & Victor, C. (2014). Does owning a pet protect older people against loneliness? BMC Geriatrics,14(1). doi:10.1186/1471-2318-14-106

The following chapter provides a guide to pet ownership at all stages, from choosing the right pet to geriatric care. Taking a proactive approach helps prevent illness and, if illness does occur, provide for early diagnosis and more successful treatment.

**What Pet to Get and When**

Choosing a pet may be the only time in our lives we get to pick a relative. Caring for a pet should begin even before you bring him or her home. Possibly the single most impactful decision you will make during the entire time you have a pet is choosing the right one. Variables to navigate include choosing dog or cat, young or adult, and purebred or mixed.

Making these kinds of decisions really is about lifestyle. The best pet to get is one that will be comfortable living in the environment and at the pace of life that is comfortable to you. The following are some important lifestyle considerations to keep in mind as you decide on your pet:

- What is your level of health and mobility?
- How much time are you at home versus working?
- Are you an "outdoorsy" person or you spend more time at home?
- How large is your living space?
- Do you have an enclosed yard?

- If you have other pets, how do they get along with other animals?
- Do you have the time and resources to brush and groom long hair or would you prefer something lower maintenance?

When most people consider getting a pet, they generally are considering a dog or cat. Other types of pets such as birds, guinea pigs, reptiles, etc. have very specific (and frequently high maintenance needs), so it is critical to do your homework before committing to any kind of pet. Failing to consider these kinds of factors can lead to a very stressful experience.

Look for a pet that naturally agrees with your pace of life. Make your decisions based on personality, not aesthetics. Forcing a square peg into a round hole is asking for trouble. Countless pets have been taken to shelters because their natural behaviors were at odds with their owner's lifestyle. For example, the person who is at work for 12 hours per day might not want to get high-energy dog that needs lots of exercise. A bored dog cooped up by himself leads to a pretty good chance the couch is going to be eaten when you come home.

The best advice for someone looking for a pet is to do research about breeds and look before you leap. If you've decided to adopt from a shelter or rescue, spend some time with the animal before you make a decision. If you choose a pet from a breeder, check references and make sure the dog or cat was bred responsibly and has excellent genetics.

## Pet Insurance

The healthcare options available to pets are more effective now than they have ever been. Top-notch care, however can get pricey. Many of the drugs and supplies used in veterinary medicine are exactly the same as those used for humans, and pharmaceutical companies don't discount a drug just because it is used on animals.

The solution to the rising costs associated with better health care is pet insurance. Like any insurance, what suits you best has to do with what kind of coverage you want, deductibles, coverage limits, etc. As a veterinarian that practices both Western and alternative medicine, I always encourage new pet owners to look for a policy that covers holistic treatment. When health issues arise, most pet owners are ready to do whatever is necessary to help their friend feel better. The last thing you ever want to do is make a treatment decision based on finances.

Insurance plans change all the time so the best advice is to do your due diligence when shopping for a policy. Ask your veterinarian which policies their clients seem most happy with. Consult with trusted friends and colleagues, and do an Internet search for, "Pet Insurance

Comparisons." As with any insurance plan, make sure to read the fine print.

## Introducing New Pets to Old

Bringing a new pet into a household with existing pets has the potential to be a stressful experience, depending on the personality of the new and existing pets. (In many cases, introductions of pets of the opposite sex seem to go more smoothly than having two of the same gender.) There are, however, ways to smooth out rough spots in the transition. The name of the game with introductions is to take it slow and be patient. There are excellent resources out there to help guide new pet introductions. Books, articles, and videos by the renowned veterinary behaviorist Dr. Sophia Yin are a great place to start.

**Dog Introductions:** The best way to introduce dogs is on neutral ground. To prevent territory aggression, have the dogs meet at the park or some other place where neither of them are on their "home turf." Have the dogs meet several times over several days before bringing the new dog home. (If this isn't possible, even a single meeting in neutral territory can be helpful.) Once home, be sure to supervise interactions until you feel comfortable a workable relationship has developed.

**Cat Introductions:** Cats are tricky when it comes to introductions because they don't like change of any kind. When bringing home an additional cat, keep it in a room with the door closed and allow the cats to sniff each other under the door. Allow the new cat to explore the house while the "old" cat is in the room. Do this for several days, and then reverse the arrangement.

It may take as long as a couple of weeks before the cats can be allowed full contact with one another. Even then, there may be some hissing and spitting. However, most cats will find a way to get along or, at least, peacefully coexist.

**Dog-Cat Introductions:** When introducing dogs to cats, take it slow. Unless the animals are particularly tolerant of the other species, it's going to take time. Cats typically feel threatened and scared, while dogs may either feel scared or want to chase the cat.

Allow the dog and cat to sniff one another under a closed door as in cat introductions. Consider keeping the dog on a leash even in the house whenever the animals are in the same room until you feel comfortable a relationship has been established. Sometimes it takes a few good swats from the cat for a dog to realize it's in their best interest to keep some distance.

**Puppy and Kitten Socialization**

The first weeks and months a puppy or kitten is at home lay the foundations of behavior for their entire lives. Your veterinarian can direct you to good local trainers if you need one. Books and videos from veterinary behaviorist Dr. Sophia Yin are excellent resources in this field as well.

**Puppy Socialization:** Socialization of young dogs is critical, especially for dogs with a tendency toward nervousness or anxiety. The optimal "window" for socialization is before they are 14 weeks old, so get started early. Introducing puppies to new experiences at a young age expands their horizons and creates a well-adjusted dog. However, this must be done under controlled conditions to prevent disease transmission and inadvertently traumatizing your dog.

Early puppy socialization classes with a trainer and taking your pup to meet friends' dogs are good ways to encourage social behavior. Any dog the puppy comes in contact with should be healthy and current on his vaccines. To prevent serious illness, never take an unvaccinated puppy to dog parks, sidewalks, or anywhere there is dog traffic you are not in control of. The risks of disease are too great.

**Kitten Socialization:** Kittens kind of socialize themselves. Since they are not out and about like dogs, there is not the same concern for disease transmission. Kittens can get a little aggressive with their play tactics, though. Even though it may be cute when they bite you when they are small, it's not so great when they weigh 15 pounds. Discourage this behavior by disengaging play when they get too rough. Then, once they calm down, you can play with them again.

## Choosing a Veterinarian

Different people have very different perspectives on medicine and health care. Some people are very "conventional" in their approach to health care where others prefer a more natural approach to medicine. Personally, I prefer to look for the benefits in both Western and holistic medicine and provide "integrative" solutions for my patients. Whatever approach you're looking for, it's important to find a veterinarian who shares your health care philosophy. You should feel confident that their treatment recommendations fit with how you want your pet's care managed.

If you are unsure what your best choice is, see what the "word on the street" is. Ask for recommendations at pet stores in your area, dog parks, and trusted friends and colleagues. If you prefer a more natural or integrative approach, the American Holistic Veterinary Association has a listing of holistic practitioners on their website: www.AHVMA.org. Just click on "Find a Vet."

## Schedule Regular Physical Examinations and Diagnostic Testing

Beyond everything you do at home, regular veterinary visits are among the most important way to make sure your pet stays healthy. As your pet gets older, you'll want to move from annual examinations to semiannual (twice yearly) examinations. The following is a general guideline and your veterinarian may make other recommendations based on your pet's health and lifestyle.

- Cats (1–10 years old): annual examinations
- Cats (10+ years old): semiannual examinations
- Small to medium breeds of dog (1–10 years old): annual examinations
- Small to medium breeds of dog (10+ years old): semiannual examinations
- Large to giant breeds of dog (1–7 years old): annual examinations
- Large to giant breeds of dog (7+ years old): semiannual examinations

During the physical exam, your veterinarian will want to run routine lab work on your pet to make sure they have not been exposed to parasites and everything is okay systemically. In many cases, the early onset of disease can be detected in blood or urine before symptoms arise. Just as with physical examinations, you'll want to move to more frequent screenings as your pet gets older from biannual (every two years) to annual testing. The following is a general guideline and your veterinarian may make other recommendations based on your pet's health and lifestyle.

# All pets, all ages: annual fecal screening for parasites

- Cats and small to medium breeds of dog (1–10 years old): biannual blood and urine testing
- Cats and small to medium breeds of dog (10+ years old): annual blood and urine testing
- Large to giant breeds of dog (1–7 years old): biannual blood and urine testing
- Large to giant breeds of dog (7+ years old): annual blood and urine testing

## Choosing the Right Procedures for Your Pet:

## Vaccines and Routine Surgical Procedures

Being a pet owner requires taking preventive steps to make sure your pet (and the pet population at large) stays healthy. While certain procedures involve short-term discomfort, the long-term benefits they provide are substantial—just like having your child vaccinated. Since pets don't plan for the future, pet owners and veterinarians must make the decisions that will provide them with a lifetime of good health.

## Declawing Cats

Let's get this procedure out of the way right now. In short, there is absolutely no legitimate reason to declaw a cat. Please don't do it. The process of declawing cats is equivalent to a person having their fingertips amputated at the last knuckle. The procedure itself is painful and it may lead to lifelong chronic pain. Declawed cats frequently become "biters" after having lost their ability to use their claws. Alternatives to declawing are scratching posts, nail trimming, and placing soft rubber caps on the nails.

**Microchipping**

Implanting a microchip in pets is commonplace in most veterinary practices. It's a tiny device about the size of a grain of rice that is implanted with a syringe. After the microchip is placed, you register the chip number with your address and contact information. Should a lost pet be brought in to a veterinary hospital, shelter, etc., the chip can be scanned and the owner contacted.

There are a couple of common misconceptions regarding microchips. Microchips cannot be used to "track" a pet because the scanners work only when they are a few inches away from the animal. Claims of cancer and other severe complications from microchips are vastly exaggerated. Some isolated incidences may have occurred but the benefits far outweigh any perceived risk.

Should a fire or natural disaster occur, owners and pets may become separated, and there is little chance for animal control to reconnect them without some kind of positive identification like a microchip. In fact, according to the Humane Society of the United States, of the 15,000 animals were rescued after Hurricane Katrina, only 3,000 were reunited with their owners.

In short, microchips are recommended for all pets.

### Routine Parasite Prevention

### Fleas and Ticks

The relative necessity for flea and tick products depends on geographic location, season, and pet's lifestyle. In hot and humid areas, the presence of these parasites can present major health problems, so good medical care necessitates regular treatment to prevent infestation. In more temperate areas, however, fleas and ticks are more of a nuisance.

There are many flea and tick products on the market and more are coming and going all the time. Which product to choose for your pet and how often to use it depends on the pet's sensitivity to fleas and how bad the fleas are in your area. Natural flea and tick control products can be useful in some situations but are generally only somewhat effective. For more comprehensive control of these pests, a more conventional treatment is generally recommended. As some over the counter products are ineffective (and sometimes toxic) please consult with your veterinarian about the best flea and tick control method for your pet.

## Gastrointestinal Worms and Deworming

Deworming generally refers to gastrointestinal worms such as hookworms and roundworms. Like all parasites, prevalence is a function of climate, with warmer, more humid areas having more severe issues. There are several ways to address GI parasitism in pets.

Regardless of where you live, an annual fecal examination is recommended to screen for parasites. If a pet is on heartworm preventive, they are likely getting dewormed regularly as part of that product. Otherwise, deworming can be accomplished on an as needed basis.

When GI parasites are confirmed via fecal testing, the best bet is to deworm your dog or cat through conventional medical means and be done with it. Although there are natural dewormers such as diatomaceous earth, they are often unreliable in the treatment of worms. They may however, be helpful as preventives.

Pharmaceutical dewormers generally take one to three days to be effective.

It is commonplace and relatively safe to use dewormers on puppies and kittens, but it may not be necessary. During the course of the puppy or kitten vaccines, your veterinarian should ask for a stool sample to check for parasites. If the test is positive, deworming is appropriate and safe. If the test is negative however, it may be just as well to hold off. Since parasites cannot always be found in every sample, it is best to have two fecal screenings done during the course of the puppy or kitten vaccines. If both are negative, there should be no need to deworm.

## Heartworm

Heartworm is a parasitic disease where worms literally live in the heart of an infected dog. (Although cats can also contract heartworm, it is rare.) Mosquitoes transmit heartworm, so disease prevalence is dependent on weather. Warm, humid climates have more heartworm cases.

Depending on where you live, you may or may not have options regarding heartworm for your dog. Temperate climates like where I live in Oakland don't have much heartworm. We do have it but it's relatively rare. The options here are to put the dog on heartworm preventive and/or or test dogs annually. Albeit highly unlikely, if a dog comes up positive, we will have caught the infestation very early making treatment easier.

In high heartworm areas such as the Southeastern US, heartworm prevention for dogs is a necessity. The odds are just too great to try and go without protection. These pets should be on heartworm prevention year-round and receive an annual heartworm test.

There are many brands of heartworm preventives on the market. They all use some version of drugs like ivermectin or milbemycin. These drugs kill the larval forms of heartworm before they become adults and set up shop in the heart. While high doses of these drugs can be dangerous to dogs, the doses used for heartworm prevention are very safe. Any risk is far outweighed by risk of contracting heartworm.

One final note regarding heartworm prevention: There is no such thing as effective natural or holistic heartworm preventive. Please don't attempt this. If a dog gets heartworm due to ineffectual prevention, the results can literally be fatal.

## Spay and Neuter

The decision when (or if) to spay or neuter a pet weighs heavily on some pet owners. If you or someone in your family is hesitant to spay or neuter your pet, you are not alone. Many people are a little hesitant. There are however, plenty of great reasons to spay or neuter and very few reasons not to. Saying, "yes" benefits your dog or cat from a physical, behavioral, and safety standpoint. It also benefits you financially and socially. Let me explain:

Spaying or neutering pets eliminates the chance of unwanted reproduction, cancer of the testicles, ovaries, and uterus, and decreases the chances of mammary (breast) cancer. In addition, neutering dogs prevents enlargement of the prostate in male dogs as they age. All of these factors improve the quality and quantity of life of dogs and cats.

Behaviorally, the reduction in testosterone and estrogen after spaying often makes pets better pets. Behaviors like aggression between animals, urine marking or spraying, and a tendency to "roam" looking for mates are all minimized. Pets are safer since they get into fewer fights, are less likely to be hit by cars, and there is far less of a chance they will be surrendered by their owners because of behavioral issues.

In addition to benefits to your pet, having them spayed or neutered benefits you as well. The decrease in fighting and elimination of medical issues as described below makes their health care easier and less expensive. It's also cheaper to license a spayed or neutered pet. Lastly, there is a social stigma to having an intact pet. If your pet is trying to mate or your female cat in heat is keeping the neighborhood awake with her howling all night, you are not winning any popularity contests.

**Perceived Drawbacks of Spay and Neuter**

There are purebred dogs and cats that are left intact in order to continue their breed. Even within this narrow field however, breeding of pets should be done very judiciously and only as often as is necessary. These pets can and should be spayed or neutered after they are successfully bred.

Perhaps the argument with the least validity is, "I want my pet to experience having a litter" or "I want my children to experience the miracle of our pet having babies." There is absolutely no evidence to suggest dogs or cats are longing for the joys of parenthood. Under most circumstances, their offspring are separated from them 8 weeks after birth anyway. It's not like they have the "joy" of watching their kids grow up!

Parents who want to breed their pets for the benefit of their children's experience would be better served to think it through a little more. A more educational alternative is for the family to volunteer at the SPCA or a local rescue group. This allows children to enjoy puppies and kittens and also realize the reality of pet overpopulation. The ASPCA estimates 2,700,000 dogs and cats are euthanized in shelters every year. There is no reason to breed more.

**What to Do and When**

Classically, veterinarians recommend spaying and neutering before pets are 6 months old. The goal here is to perform the surgery before they hit puberty. This eliminates most hormonally associated behavioral issues and, in females, eliminates the chances of mammary (breast) cancer later in life. Although this has been "written in stone" in the veterinary community for many years, new research is about to shake things up.

Recent studies however indicate certain breeds of dogs have lower incidences of specific cancers, orthopedic disease, urinary incontinence, and age-related cognitive decline if they are spayed or neutered later. In other words, waiting longer leads to better health in the long term. While there are definitely differences between the breeds, there does appear to be a trend towards better health in pets that were spayed or neutered later. To date, the published studies have only evaluated Golden Retrievers, Labrador Retrievers, and German Shepherds and it is unknown if these trends will hold true with all breeds of dogs.

There have been no similar studies done in cats and the behavioral issues associated with intact male and female cats is so significant, it would be unrealistic to expect the majority of pet owners to "stick it out" and wait to spay and neuter.

In the final analysis the question is really not if you should spay or neuter your pet, but when. Based on what we know as of 2018, recommendations for spay and neuter are as follows:

- Small to medium dogs: Spay or neuter at 12 to 18 months of age
- Large or giant breeds: Spay or neuter at 18 to 24

months of age
- Cats: Spay or neuter on or around 6 months of age

Lastly, if an intact male dog does not have behavioral issues, there is no absolute necessity to neuter him. Careful veterinary monitoring for the development of testicular cancer or prostate enlargement as he gets older may necessitate neutering down the road. Outside of these concerns, leaving males intact poses no major health risks. The same cannot be said for females who run the risk of ovarian, uterine, or mammary cancer as well as uterine infections, which can be life-threatening. They should be spayed as described above.

## A Guide to Appropriate Vaccination

Dog and cat owners are often unclear about what to vaccinate their pets for and how often. In truth, the veterinary community is not in complete agreement on the topic. There are several reasons for the disparity amongst veterinarians that range from disagreement between researchers to simple unwillingness to change.

It is true that vaccines are not benign drugs. Under normal circumstances, vaccines stimulate the immune system, leading to antibody production and effective immunity against disease. However, the body might respond to a vaccine with excessive or aberrant immune stimulation, and this may lead to medical issues in your pet. Although the research is ongoing and not conclusive, vaccines in pets have been implicated in the onset of autoimmune diseases and cancerous processes. Cats are susceptible to a cancer called feline injection-site sarcoma, which are aggressive tumors that require extensive treatment. However, the risk to your cat is as low as 1 in 10,000.

Despite any controversy, appropriately administered vaccines are absolutely necessary. The fact is, without protection from diseases like canine distemper and parvo, many dogs would die before reaching adulthood. The same is true for cats with panleukopenia, and both species are susceptible to rabies.

Vaccines are effective and have saved countless pets. Like every other drug however, vaccines should be used judiciously.

**Vaccine Do's and Don'ts**

The big "don't" when it comes to vaccines is: **don't overvaccinate**. To that end, in the following sections, I discuss the difference between core and non-core canine and feline vaccinations as well as vaccine titers.

Core vaccines are the ones that should be given to all pets to protect them from life-threatening diseases. The only exception are pets with an underlying medical condition that precludes the ability to safely vaccinate; such decisions should be made with your veterinarian based on what is safest for your pet.

Non-core vaccinations are available for pets whose lifestyle may put them in contact with specific diseases. These non-core vaccines are recommended for certain animals based largely on lifestyle and geographic location.

Vaccine titers are a means by which your pet's level of immunity can be measured through a blood sample. It measures the level of antibodies that the animal's immune system has produced in response to a vaccine against a specific disease. Through this method, we can determine whether your pet is protected.

The bottom line is, vaccinate for what is absolutely necessary based on core vaccination protocols, legal necessities, and your pet's lifestyle. Don't vaccinate for diseases your pet will never come in contact with. To prevent adverse reactions, it is best if pets receive no more than two vaccines at any one time, and wait at least one month before giving the next vaccinations. As they get older, dogs and cats may need fewer vaccines. Older pets tend to be outside less and have less direct contact with other animals. Talk with your veterinarian about what is necessary for your pet at the stage of life he or she is currently in.

## Core Canine (Dog) Vaccines

The vaccine schedules discussed below are guidelines for safe and effective vaccination. Timing and protocol variation based on the needs of an individual pet are commonplace. Consult with your veterinarian about what is best for your dog.

**Canine distemper and parvo vaccination:** Canine distemper and parvo (short for canine parvovirus type 2) are deadly viruses that commonly affect younger, unvaccinated dogs. Distemper often causes severe respiratory infection and sometimes neurologic disease; it is most commonly transmitted through coughing dogs. Parvo causes severe gastrointestinal disease, including vomiting and profound bloody diarrhea that is infectious to other dogs.

Because parvo is so contagious, it is critical that puppies not be allowed to go anywhere with a lot of dog traffic and/or stray dogs. Until they are fully vaccinated, keep their interactions restricted to controlled environments like puppy class or friends' houses.

There are many vaccines available that protect against distemper and parvo. However, Nobivac made by Intervet/ Merck is the only one that contains only distemper and parvo. All others are combined with vaccinations against diseases such as leptospirosis, canine adenovirus, and parainfluenza. I believe that vaccines combining three, four, or even five different diseases are unnecessary because they may increase the chances of adverse reactions.

Canine distemper and parvo titers can be used to determine the necessity of further vaccinations after the initial core vaccine series. Dogs who show adequate antibody levels to distemper and parvo are presumed to be immune and need no further vaccinations; however, they will need to be retested every three years.

- Puppies need three doses at 3- to 4-week intervals starting at 8 to 10 weeks of age—for example, at 8, 12, and 16 weeks of age.
- One-year-old dogs should have a distemper-parvo titer (see below) or a single vaccine. The Nobivac vaccine will have a three-year duration.
- Starting at one or four years old, distemper-parvo titers are recommended every three years.

**Rabies vaccination:** Most people are at least passingly familiar with rabies. This virus, which is transmitted through the saliva of an infected animal, is 100 percent fatal to pets. Only a handful of humans have ever survived a rabies infection, and because of its transmissibility to humans, rabies vaccinations in dogs are legally required. Depending on where you live, rabies vaccination may be required for cats as well. Medical exemptions can be granted based on approval of the local animal services or public health departments.

The legal specifics of when rabies vaccines need to be given vary by geographic location. Your veterinarian will let you know what the requirements are.

Rabies vaccine titers are available and often required for the transportation of dogs overseas. Although a rabies titer does indicate protection from the rabies virus, it is not acceptable as an alternative to vaccination in the eyes of the law.

There are two different kinds of rabies titers. If you are travelling overseas, the Fluorescent Antibody Virus Neutralization (FAVN) test may be required. If the titer is being used to demonstrate immunity for reasons other than travel, Rapid Fluorescent Foci Inhibition Test (RFFIT) is recommended. It can take weeks to get rabies titer results back, so be sure to plan ahead with regards to travel.

- Puppies should have a rabies vaccine between 16 and 20 weeks of age, as per local ordinance.
- A one-year booster is required in most areas, and then the vaccine is required every three years.
- Rabies vaccine titers are often required for overseas transport of your pet. They are not a legal substitute for vaccination.

## Non-Core Canine Vaccines

**Leptospirosis:** Leptospirosis is a bacterial disease transmitted through the urine of infected animals. It is contracted when a dog drinks from a contaminated water source such as a puddle. Leptospirosis infections can be quite serious and lead to liver or kidney failure (see Chapters 18 and 19). It is also transmissible to humans.

Dogs spending a lot of time outdoors may be at greater risk for leptospirosis. Your veterinarian can discuss with you the relative incidence in your area. It is possible for vaccinated dogs to get leptospirosis.

- Initially, dogs are given two vaccines, approximately one month apart.
- A booster vaccine is required annually to maintain immunity.

**Bordetella:** Bordetella bronchiseptica is a bacterium that causes the disease colloquially known as "kennel cough." However, saying a dog has "kennel cough" is like saying a person has "a cold." Kennel cough is simply a description of symptoms that can be caused by many different organisms. The Bordetella vaccine protects against only one bacterial organism.

Kennel cough is transmitted through the air when infected dogs cough, which is why transmission is most common in enclosed areas such as boarding facilities. To help prevent outbreaks, the vaccine is frequently required by boarding, daycare, and grooming facilities.

The vast majority of dogs who get kennel cough recover with no treatment or with a short course of antibiotics and cough suppressants. Severe disease from kennel cough caused by secondary pneumonia is rare and the vaccine does not prevent all dogs from getting sick.

- Bordetella vaccines can be oral, intranasal, or injectable. The oral or intranasal forms are best.
- Vaccination is needed every 6 to 12 months, depending on risk assessment and the requirements of any facilities that you frequent.

**Canine Influenza:** Canine influenza is a strain of flu that specifically infects dogs. As is the case with the flu in people, most dogs will recover although a small population of them can get very sick and even potentially die. Much like Bordetella (above), canine influenza is frequently transmitted in enclosed, high population density environments like boarding facilities, groomers, etc. If canine influenza is prevalent in your geographic area, your veterinarian may recommend vaccination.

- Initial vaccination with canine influenza requires two vaccines given 2-4 weeks apart
- Booster vaccinations for at-risk dogs are given

annually
- *Note: Canine Influenza is NOT transmissible to humans

**Lyme**: Lyme is a bacterial disease transmitted by ticks, so along with vaccination, tick control is a major part of Lyme prevention. The disease affects both dogs and humans, although humans tend to get the worst of it. The prevalence of Lyme disease varies greatly by geographic region. Depending on where you live, a Lyme vaccination may be considered a core vaccine.

- Initial vaccination is a series of two vaccines given one month apart, and then a third given six months later.
- Annual boosters are recommended to maintain immunity.
- Vaccinated dogs will sometimes show a "false positive" on Lyme testing
- *Note: Lyme cannot be transmitted from dogs to humans. A bite from an infected tick is required for an individual to get Lyme disease.

**Rattlesnake Toxoid:** Obviously, there is no vaccine that is going to prevent a snake from biting a nosy dog. The rattlesnake toxoid was developed to help minimize the severity of rattlesnake bites in dogs. "Vaccinated" dogs tend to have less severe reactions to rattlesnake venom and may need less antivenin. However, any dog bitten by a rattlesnake needs immediate medical attention, regardless of vaccination status.

- Dogs living in rattlesnake endemic areas, or those who travel to the backcountry, may benefit from vaccination.
- The rattlesnake vaccine is initially given as a series of two vaccines, one month apart. Boosters are recommended every 6 to 12 months depending on the level of risk.
- If the booster is given annually, it is best to give it in the spring, when snakes have the most venom and bites are potentially the most dangerous.

**Core Feline (Cat) Vaccines**

The vaccine schedules discussed below are guidelines for safe and effective vaccination. Timing and protocol variation based on the needs of an individual pet are commonplace. Consult with your veterinarian about what is best for your kitty.

**FVRCP**: FVRCP is a combination vaccine that protects against feline viral rhinotracheitis (FVR), feline calicivirus (C), and panleukopenia (P). Rhinotracheitis and calicivirus cause upper respiratory symptoms rather like bad head colds and are rarely life-threatening. Panleukopenia, however, is similar to parvo in dogs, a potentially fatal disease that causes severe GI distress.

Feline panleukopenia titers can be used to determine the necessity of further vaccinations after the initial core vaccine series. Cats who show adequate antibody levels to panleukopenia are presumed to be immune. There is no titer for rhinotracheitis or calcivirus.

- Kittens are usually given three doses at 3- to 4-week intervals, usually at 8, 12, and 16 weeks. Alternatively, two vaccines can be given when they are 8 or 9 weeks old, and then at 12 or 13 weeks old, as long as they stay strictly indoors so their disease exposure prior to completing their vaccine series is minimal.
- A booster vaccine at one year of age is effective for three years. You may use a panleukopenia titer afterward to determine whether further vaccinations are needed.
- Adult cats who are allowed outdoors may benefit from an FVRCP booster every three years, as protection against upper respiratory viruses.

**Rabies**: Most people are at least passingly familiar with rabies. This virus, which is transmitted through the saliva of an infected animal, is 100 percent fatal to pets. Only a handful of humans have ever survived a rabies infection, and because of its transmissibility to human, rabies vaccinations in cats are legally required. However, medical exemptions can be granted based on approval of the local animal services or public health departments. The legal specifics of when rabies vaccines need to be given vary by geographic location. Your veterinarian will let you know what the requirements are.

There are several rabies vaccines available. Purevax made by Merial seems to cause the fewest reactions. Purevax vaccines are available as both one-year and three-year protection duration.

Rabies vaccine titers are available and often required for the transportation of cats overseas. Although a rabies titer does indicate protection from the rabies virus, it is not acceptable as an alternative to vaccination in the eyes of the law.

There are two different kinds of rabies titers. If you are travelling overseas, the Fluorescent Antibody Virus Neutralization (FAVN) test may be required. If the titer is being used to demonstrate immunity for reasons other than travel, Rapid Fluorescent Foci Inhibition Test (RFFIT) is recommended. It can take weeks to get rabies titer results back, so be sure to plan ahead with regards to travel.

- All kittens should be given a rabies vaccination between 16 and 20 weeks of age.
- Strictly indoor cats do not need a rabies booster.

(The single vaccine as a kitten may help provide some immunity in case the cat gets outside.)

- Cats allowed outdoors should have a booster at one year, and then every one or three years, depending on the vaccine used.
- Rabies vaccine titers are often required for overseas transport of your pet. They are not a legal substitute for vaccination.

**Non-Core Feline Vaccines**

**Feline leukemia:** Feline leukemia virus (FeLV) is a retrovirus much like human immunodeficiency virus (HIV) in humans. Despite the name, the virus rarely causes leukemia, but it can lead to immune dysfunction and secondary illness in much the same way HIV progresses to acquired immune deficiency syndrome (AIDS). Also similar to HIV, it can take years for cats infected with FeLV to show any symptoms of disease.

FeLV is contracted through the bite or scratch from an infected cat. "Casual" contact is not generally considered a major risk for contracting the disease, and cats living in the same household for years may not transmit the virus from one to the other. Regardless, infected cats should be kept strictly indoors to prevent transmission. Outdoor cats and cats living with an FeLV-infected cat should be vaccinated.

- Kittens should initially be given two vaccines, approximately one month apart.
- A booster vaccine is needed at one year of age and every three years afterward.

**Feline Immunodeficiency Virus:**

Feline immunodeficiency virus (FIV) is a retrovirus like FeLV. Over time, the virus suppresses the immune system, leading other conditions like infections and organ disease. Just like FeLV, FIV infection can take years to show symptoms. FIV is usually contracted through the bite or scratch from an infected cat, and "casual" contact is not generally considered a risk for contracting the disease.

There are two problems with the FIV vaccine: (1) It is not particularly effective, and (2) FIV-vaccinated cats will test positive for FIV. Unfortunately, this can lead to FIV-vaccinated cats that turn up at shelters being euthanized under suspicion of being FIV positive. For these reasons, vaccinating for FIV is not recommended.

**Feeding Dogs and Cats For a Lifetime of Good Health**

**Deciphering Dog and Cat Diets**

"Let food be thy medicine and medicine be thy food." When Hippocrates said this around 2500 years ago, food and medicine were largely one in the same. The miracles of modern science have since created a separation between our food and medicine. While no one can deny how humans and animals benefit from the current state of our medical care, we have, in some respects, lost our way with regards to how critical nutrition is to preventing and treating disease.

All animals evolved to function optimally when they are provided with a specific set of nutrients. We all need water, proteins, fats, vitamins, minerals, etc. to survive. The closer an animal comes to consuming these nutrients in the quantities, formats, and varieties that satisfy biological requirements, the more healthy their body tends to be.

Back in Hippocrates' day, certain foods (and thus certain nutrients) may have been scarce based on season, weather, and demand. The result could have been ill health related to poor nutrition. In the modern era, we do not have to search far and wide for our basic nutritional requirements. We have our own issues however such excessive intake of calories, carbohydrates, and fats. Highly processed foods deplete nutritional value. The general state of our food industry may be providing foods with fewer inherent nutrients and genetically modified foods create a whole additional layer of complexity and concern. The result of the modern diet is often obesity, chronic inflammation, and the onset of disease related to imbalanced nutrition.

As an integrative practice veterinarian, one of the most frequent questions I encounter is, "What is the best food to feed?" The answer to this question depends on many factors such as age, breed, current state of health, and lifestyle. That said, one generalization can be made: The closer we get our pets to eating a fresh, whole food diet, the better their health tends to be.

Hopefully, this is not a shocking statement to anyone. We all evolved to eat fresh, whole foods. It does not take a PhD in nutrition to realize that the biological "machine" functions best with this kind of fuel. While not all pet foods on the market provide optimal nutrition, thankfully there are quite a few good options available.

There are multiple formats of foods out there to offer our pets. Nutritionally speaking, some are better than others. Let's look at them one by one and discuss their merits and potential shortcomings. Remember, some individuals will do better on certain food than others.

### Dry Food (Kibble)

Kibble is by far the most popular format of food. Most kibble is manufactured through the process of extrusion.

### Pros

- You can't beat the convenience. Just open the bag and pour into the bowl.

- It is inexpensive.
- The food has a long shelf life.

## Cons

- It's made in a high-temperature process, which may affect the nutrient profile.
- This method of production leads to the presence of toxic by-products like Maillard reaction products (MRPs) and advanced glycation endproducts (AGEs).
- The level and type of preservatives used in dry food varies. Some foods use natural preservatives such as mixed tocopherols and rosemary extract. Others use artificial (and potentially harmful) preservatives such as ethoxyquin.
- Kibble is by definition high in carbohydrates, even the "low-carb" and "grain-free" varieties. High-carbohydrate diets can lead to weight gain and chronic inflammation. Note: Some smaller companies have begun to introduce baked (rather than extruded) kibble that is lower in carbohydrates.
- The low-moisture content in kibble may also lead to pets (particularly cats) having chronic mild dehydration, which can affect health in both the short and long term.

## Canned Diets

There is a range of canned diets from super premium to very low quality. It is important to read ingredient labels and know what you are buying.

### Pros

- Canned foods are convenient and have a long shelf life.
- The high moisture content helps provide extra water in the diet (which is a benefit over dry foods).
- Canned foods are lower in carbohydrates than kibble. (Note: Canned foods containing grains such as rice will have higher levels of carbohydrates.)

### Cons

- Canned foods are by necessity processed at very high temperatures, which leads to the presence of MRPs and AGEs. The process may also result in the loss of micronutrients and enzymes that are beneficial for your pet.
- Metals or plastics (from the can or the can liner) can potentially leach into the food.

## Low-Temperature Processed Foods

These diets are generally freeze-dried or dehydrated versions of fresh, whole-food diets. Many pet stores carry them.

### Pros

- Freeze-dried diets retain many of the benefits of fresh, raw diets. The low-temperature processing preserves micronutrients that might be lost in higher temperature methods. (Note that dehydration is a somewhat higher temperature process than freeze drying but is far more preferable to kibble or cans.)
- Since water is added to the diet before feeding, moisture content is controlled, which helps make sure pets are getting enough water.
- As with the fresh-food diets, these diets tend to be made with high-quality ingredients.
- These diets have a long shelf life at room temperature.
- Several freeze-dried pet foods are certified pathogen-free when packaged. (This means they are tested and found free of bacterial contamination.)

### Cons

- Freeze-dried raw products carry the risk of cross-contamination. Be careful in households with small children or immune-compromised people. (Cross-contamination refers to exposure to bacteria from secondary contact. In other words, if the dog eats his raw food and then licks someone in the face or someone touches the plate the food was on and then puts their fingers in their mouth.)

- These products tend to be more costly than kibble and cans, which can sometimes present a financial challenge for people with a large dog or multiple pets.

## Fresh-Food Diets

These diets include either raw or lightly cooked foods purchased fresh or frozen or made at home using a balanced recipe.

## Pros

- A balanced, fresh, whole-food diet contains excellent nutrition and high-moisture content while minimizing exposure to artificial ingredients and preservatives.
- The lack of high-temperature processing preserves micronutrients and enzymes that may be lost in other food formats. Many pets with chronic inflammatory conditions, such as allergies or inflammatory bowel disease (IBD), fare better on fresh-food diets.

- These diets tend to be made with high-quality ingredients.
- Several raw pet foods are certified pathogen-free when packaged. This means they are tested and found free of bacterial contamination.
- When made at home, fresh-food diets can be reasonably cost-effective.

**Cons**

- Fresh food is perishable and requires frequent preparation and/or significant freezer space for storage.
- Appropriate precautions should be taken when handling and feeding raw meat regardless of prior testing for bacteria. Potential cross-contamination to humans should be considered. Be careful in households with small children or immune-compromised people.
- Homemade fresh food diets can be cost effective but time consuming to prepare.
- When purchased premade in stores, these diets can be expensive for larger dogs or in multiple-pet households.

**The Bottom Line: Good vs. Optimal**

Most good-quality pet food, regardless of format, provides good nutrition. The "super premium" brands of food use excellent ingredients. Once it is processed into cans or kibble, though, some of the nutrition is lost. Optimal nutrition can only be achieved through fresh, whole-food diets. While the particular ingredients and nutrient profiles of optimal diets will vary with species, age, and medical conditions, the future is leaving kibble and canned diets behind in the distance.

In our quest for optimal nutrition, practicality must play a role. (This is the real world, after all.) No doubt we would all be healthier if we had a private chef preparing all of our meals with the best and freshest ingredients. Sadly (for me, at least), this is not the reality. When it comes to our pets, store-bought foods are practical. In these cases, frozen raw, freeze-dried, or dehydrated foods that are readily available provide excellent options that are far superior to kibble and cans.

For those with the time and interest, well-constructed, home-prepared diets are usually the best way to feed a dog or cat. Preparing food at home means you are in control of the quality and freshness of ingredients and the food can be custom-tailored to your pet's needs. Recipes must, however, be properly nutritionally balanced by a trained nutritionist. The road to poor nutrition is often paved with the good intentions of loving pet owners. Long-term feeding of an unbalanced diet can lead to serious medical consequences. Thus, creating a home-prepared diet is absolutely not the time to wing it.

## Technology for Pets

Regardless of how you may feel about it, we live in a technological society. Cell phones, computers, and gadgets of all kinds regularly govern our lives. While our pets are far less dependent on tech than we are, there are some new innovations that your pets might really benefit from and even enjoy.

**Chips and Trackers:** Microchips (as described above) have been around for years and are responsible for thousands of pets being reunited with owners after being lost. The shortcoming of microchips however are that in order to read the chip, a scanner has to be within inches of the animal. Thus microchips only help once the lost pet has been found and scanned.

More recently however, GPS tracking devices for pets have been developed. These products are small enough to be put on a pet's collar. Once set, the tracker allows pet owners to locate their pet on their cell phone or computer. They can also be set to alert the owner when the pet leaves a pre-designated area such as your yard.

**Feeding:** Automatic food bowls are available for pet owners that may have to miss feeding time. These bowls however, generally only work for dry food. As we discussed previously, dry food is not optimal nutrition and thus their application is limited for pet owners feeding fresh, whole food diets.

**Entertainment:** Did you know there is TV for pets now? Yes, your dog can tune in to programming specifically designed for animals. Dog TV (dogtv.com) will give your pet something to watch while you are out of the house.

**Exercise:** One of the great health benefits of owning a dog is walking. The act of walking your dog provides emotional, social, and physical benefits. There may be times however when you are unable to get your dog out for a walk. Internet-based services like Rover.com can schedule a dog walker to come and walk your dog(s) for you. The company does all of the background checking for you. And if that is not enough, prototypes are in development for robotic dog walkers. Yes, I am serious.

**Medical Technology:** At-home and point of care medical devices are the future of medicine and veterinary medicine is no exception. Many of the same GPS locating devices described above also help monitor your pet's health. They can keep track of activity and alert you if there are any changes in his/her patterns. In addition, the technology now exists for pet owners to monitor their pets for the presence of urinary tract infections, diabetic monitoring, and even EKG monitoring for pets with heart conditions.

## Ensuring Your Pet's Future

Having a pet provides us with unconditional love in ways

only they can provide. In exchange, we provide them with love in return as well as safety and security. Depending on the breed and species, life expectancy of dogs and cats tends to be between 10 and 20 years. That's a long time and a lot can happen with our own health during that time. It is important to consider your pet's future should something happen that would make it impossible for you to care for them.

As with all issues of estate planning, deciding what will become of your pets ahead of time is, by far, your best course of action. In many cases, family members or close friends will take on pets when their primary owner can no longer care for them. In circumstances where this is not possible, making a contingency plan for your pet could literally be a life or death decision for them. Middle-aged to older pets frequently do not get adopted from animal shelters.

If there is no family member or friend who can take care of your pet, consider making an arrangement with a shelter or rescue group. If you are able, you might make arrangements to leave a grant or endowment to a rescue group in exchange for them agreeing to see that your pets are well taken care of. Alternatively, you may consider volunteering at a shelter or rescue group. Beyond being a rewarding experience and a way to help animals, you may be able to make connections to ensure your pets are cared for should something happen to you.

## End of Life Care and Moving Forward

## Why Is This So Difficult?

It's inevitable. We pretend every day that it is not... but it is. Our pet's physical bodies (not to mention our own) cannot go on forever. The illusion that the day will never come is just that, an illusion. Unless we, as pet owners, are very old or very unlucky, we will have to face end of life issues with our pets. For many people, the emotional complexities of the experience are more than they are prepared for.

Given these circumstances, is it any wonder that we have such a hard time letting go?

## The day you find out what "it" is going to be

It's a surreal moment when you find out what your pet is likely going to die from. With the initial diagnosis of cancer, kidney failure, or some other incurable condition, the illusion is dispelled and the veil is lifted. Their life is going to end and you are going to have to figure a way to deal with it. While the details of the process tend to be specific to the individual patient and pet owner, the general plan is fairly constant- Maintain quality of life for as long as possible, decide when to say "when", and begin to cope and move on once they have passed.

## Quality of Life Care

For most veterinarians and pet owners, quality of life is really the only parameter that matters. We can talk all day about blood work and biopsies, but none of it holds a candle to the discussion of quality of life. Quality of life can be roughly divided into two categories: 1) The level of physical pain/ discomfort the pet is experiencing, and 2) How a pet's day-to-day experience is compared to what it was prior to their getting sick.

## Assessing and Treating Pain

Assessing pain and discomfort in animals can be difficult, even for veterinarians. Although they have been domesticated for thousands of years, our pets retain much of their ancestor's sensibilities. A wild animal that looks sick or injured is going to be targeted by predators. As such, animals are very good at hiding their symptoms. This is why many animals are diagnosed in the later stages of their illness. They are doing everything they can to project the image that they are OK. It is often only when they can no longer maintain the charade that we are able to see outward signs of them being sick or being in pain.

Given their "hard-wired" nature, we can't count on our pets to cry out in pain or give us other obvious cues when they are hurting or uncomfortable. Fortunately, there are subtle changes in behavior we can look for that will let us in on some of their secrets. In the case of dogs and cats, pain may be manifested as behavioral changes such as hiding or isolating themselves from people or other animals. In many cases, a pet will lay in places they have never gone to before. Lack of appetite can also sometimes be a sign of discomfort. Increases in respiration rate and heart rate are also possible indicators of pain.

There are many options for treating a pet in pain. On the pharmaceutical side, we have non-steroidal anti-inflammatories (Rimadyl®, Metacam®, etc), steroids (prednisone), opiates (fentanyl, morphine, buprenorphine), and other pain-relieving drugs such as tramadol and gabapentin. Which medication or combination of medications is appropriate is a discussion to have with your veterinarian.

Traversing beyond the pharmaceutical, complementary and alternative care can be very helpful in managing pain and with the hospice aspect of veterinary care in general. Acupuncture for example, can help with pain as well as with anxiety and in supporting appetite in ailing pets. There are many Chinese and Western herbal formulas that can be beneficial in alleviating pain and supporting quality of life as well. For those who are interested in exploring complementary and alternative care options, finding a veterinarian with experience in these areas is the best way to go. The website for the American Holistic

Veterinary Medical Association (www.ahvma.org) is an excellent resource for finding a trained veterinarian in your area.

## Evaluating Quality of Life

Quality of life evaluation can be challenging. Our judgment may be clouded by emotion, unrealistic hopes and "seeing what we want to see." That said, however, making this determination is a vital component of providing our pets with the soft landing they deserve.

Begin by determining your definition of quality of life. It is different for everyone. Quality of life should be defined by the level of pain/ discomfort the animal is in (see above), and what their day-to-day existence looks like. Specifically, ask yourself the following questions:

- What activities is my pet doing during the day?
- Is he/she eating and drinking normally?
- How does his/her day now compare to what it looked like prior to them getting sick?
- Considering the things he/she used to do for fun, how many of those things are still going on?
- Is he/she interactive or withdrawn?
- Is he/she "living" or just eating, drinking, and sleeping?

One of the most common questions pet owners ask in

these situations is how to tell when it's time to consider euthanasia. My recommendation is to consider their pet's quality of life at this moment and decide what parameters will lead them to conclude their quality of life has become overly compromised.

While there are no right or wrong answers, it is advisable (if possible) to consider these parameters while your pet is stable and feeling relatively good. This allows you to consider the situation with a relative minimum of emotion. The goal is to determine a "line in the sand" which, once crossed, would indicate that euthanasia should be considered. Remember, none of this is written in stone. You can change your mind and your parameters along the way. It's just a good idea to have a starting point that was made during a calm, rational moment.

## When Quality of Life Deteriorates

There will come a time when medical options are exhausted, the line in the sand has been crossed and decisions have to be made. This is the toughest part of the journey: The decision of when to say "when."

There is perhaps no more personal decision someone can make than the decision of when to euthanize. It cuts to the core of our philosophy, religion and our ability to end the suffering of a loved one despite the level of emotional pain it causes us. Clearly, this is not a decision that is made lightly, and to the extent that it is possible, it should be a decision you feel good about. Remember, our pets provide us with unconditional love for their entire lives. They deserve not to suffer. This is the last, best favor you can do for them.

Once the decision has been made, there are just a few secondary considerations. The first is location. The veterinary office is always an option although many people prefer in-home euthanasia due to more comfortable surroundings for the pet and the entire family. Second, is deciding to be present during part or all of the process. This is a very personal decision. Do what feels right for you. Lastly is the question of what to do afterwards. Most veterinarians provide services for cremation of pets. People can either request the ashes returned or to be scattered. Burial at home is also an option although it is advisable to check local ordinances prior to doing so.

The process of euthanasia generally involves two steps. Usually, the pet is sedated with an appropriate sedative as determined by the veterinarian. The goal is to minimize any stress or anxiety the pet may be experiencing. We want this to be as peaceful a process as possible. Once the sedation has taken effect, an intravenous injection is given. This injection is a very large dose of anesthesia. The result is the pet becomes so deeply anesthetized that their body systems stop. The process takes only a matter of seconds and they are unconscious well before their heart stops beating. There is no pain. Only peace.

## Immediately After

The moments immediately following euthanasia have been described as "surreal," "sudden" and occasionally "relief." For most people, being witness to the end of the life of a loved one is sacred and profound. If you are compelled to, take a few moments and appreciate with gratitude the love and joy you have experienced with your pet. Thank them for all they have given you and be assured you gave them the same in return.

## Moving Forward

Even in situations where euthanasia has long been discussed, the finality of it all can be overwhelming. One moment they are with us, and in the next moment, they are gone. The reality that we as pet owners had a hand in when and how that happened affects people in different ways. The only constant is, we must go through it.

Grieving is part of life. We all lose loved ones along the way. How to cope with the loss depends on people's individual preferences and communication styles.

Being a veterinarian, I have had the opportunity to speak with many pet owners over the years and hear how they have found closure after the loss of a beloved pet. In many cases, people rely on family members and friends to help them through the loss. For those who have other animals in their lives, the consistency of unconditional love from them can provide a great level of comfort. In addition, many communities have pet loss support groups that offer a place for people to find one another and share their experiences.

As is the case with the loss of a human family member, a ceremony of remembrance can provide comfort and solace. Ceremonies can range from the highly spiritual to something resembling an Irish wake. Some people choose to scatter their pet's ashes in a favorite spot while others take advantage of a biodegradable urn containing a tree seed. The urn is buried and a tree grows up from the ashes. Caring for the young seedling as it grows into a tree is a wonderful way to remember a lost pet and continue a relationship with them through nature.

There may come a day, when you are ready to consider allowing another loving pet into your life. For some of us it takes longer than others to be ready. The reality is: in many cases we have nothing to do with it. Your new pet may find you when you least expect it. Regardless of the steps one takes through the grieving process, it is vital to remember all of the love and joy that you and your pet provided one another.

# 16. The Crazy but Very Possible Future

- **Avatar – Anywhere is possible (ANA) XPRIZE** per the site "The $10M ANA Avatar XPRIZE is a four-year global competition focused on the development of an Avatar System that will transport a human's sense, actions, and presence to a remote location in real time, leading to a more connected world." Imagine having an avatar suite in your home (think of a robot that looks human), various people could sign into the avatar suite to help you with cooking, therapy, cleaning, and even companionship. You would only pay for the services they offered and your safety is maintained at all times as they are never really in your house, they are only operating the avatar robot remotely. While this technology is several years away, I would expect avatars to be the new appliance of the future, just as a washing machine, oven and vacuum cleaner improved our lives so will this technology.

- **Fallskip** – Fallskip, developed in Spain allows for a risk assessment to be quickly and accurately completed using a belt that you put around your waist with a smartphone (Android). Healthcare professionals can objectively measure your risk of falling, which is not only a huge fear as we age but according to the Centers for Disease Control and Prevention (CDC), **falls** are the number one cause of fatal and non-fatal injuries in Americans aged 65 and older. Precision medicine or personalized medicine can then be created to help you with customizable therapy or exercise to reduce the risk of falling.

- **Spider Silk**– Spider silk is stronger than steel but has yet to be able to be mass produced like silk, however this is changing. Bolt Threads has finally cracked how to mass produce it. This will change forever what our clothes, furniture, wall coverings and flooring etc are made of and how durable similar to when nylon was introduced. Currently, Adidas has used spider silk in a prototype running shoe, U.S. Army is testing for ballistics protection. and The North Face is using for a lightweight coat.

- **Brown Algae Memory Booster** – This memory-boosting drug just completed Phase 3 clinical trials (which is right before it hits the market and can be purchased by the public) for Alzheimer's and dementia. GV-971 was developed by the Ocean University of China, Shanghai Institute of Materia Medica Extracted from brown algae. The drug has also shown that it can regulate the immune system, reduce neuroinflammation and improve cognition.

- **Facial Recognition** – Facial recognition looks at 30,000 separate infrared points that can determine you from another. The technology is nothing new as Las Vegas casinos have used this for years as well as China who is currently working to identify its 1.4 Billion citizens in seconds. The positive implications are personalized concierge shopping, going to a restaurant, hotel or the doctor. in this situation, facial recognition would allow others that are there to help, diagnose and serve you to have information of your likes, dislikes, health issues, etc in milliseconds without even having to ask you, look something up or have a photographic memory. Imagine having your glasses fitted with facial recognition automatically telling you the names of everyone at the party. Chinese police officers already use these glasses.

- **Alzheimer's and A.I.**- uMETHOD Health has developed artificial intelligence (AI) for precision medicine to treat and diagnose Alzheimer's.

- **Tooth Sensor** – A wearable on the tooth, could improve your health. Tufts University has developed a millimeter-sized sensor that can detect sugar, salt, and alcohol. "The team plans to refine the sensor to the point where it will be able to detect and measure all kinds of nutrients, and maybe even biochemicals too" per SingularityHub. This wearable tooth sensor could help you refine what you need to eat more of, less of and the supplements you need to take to improve your wellbeing and be your best you.

- **Memory Boosting Cells** – Wake Forest Baptist Medical Center has produced resulted were they were able to boost memory by 37%. Essentially the researchers identify and take out an individual's brain cell pattern for memory and then reinsert it back in, this increases the strength of the memory and makes it easier to recall.
- **Cancer-detecting A.I.** – Artificial Intelligence has been proven to detect skin cancer, metastatic breast cancer, colorectal cancer, and other cancers better than doctors. As the technology becomes more widely available, precision medicine along with early detection should substantially increase the positive outcomes of treatment.
- **Muse EEG sunglasses** – Sunglasses with built-in EEG that will be able to help you count your steps, record your EEG and document your heart rate. Creating biofeedback so that you can have a better quality of life.
- **NanoDrops** – Researchers in Israel are developing nanodrops that would correct vision for most eyesight problems such as nearsightedness, farsightedness, astigmatism, and presbyopia, making glasses obsolete.

## GE 2025 Future of Appliances

I had the honor of interviewing General Electric's chief

designer for appliances, Paul Hanely, regarding the vision they have laid out for how technology will impact the home through appliance design.

In GE's Home 2025 Appliances of the Future, in their vision, they created personas explaining the needs and then the technology that could help those needs for each persona. Multi-tasking Maria and Reluctant Roberto are GE's senior personas. Maria is 61 years old has raised her family, and has her 84-year-old father living with her. The vision is that technology can ease Maria's burden and Roberto's guilt of having his daughter take care of him.

While interviewing Paul regarding how quickly these technologies will be available, it was clear that market demand, which will reduce cost, will be the key. The technology is not farfetched. Most of it exists today in various forms. Tying the various technologies together into a seamless system that is cost-effective will be the key to mass adoption.

For instance, GE already has an oven that is a four-in-one unit that uses Advantium technology. Sounds like something out of *Star Trek*, but it's been around since 1999.

According to GE, "Advantium technology harnesses the power of light. The outside of the food is cooked like a conventional oven, with radiant heat produced by halogen bulbs above and below the food. This halogen-produced heat receives a boost of microwave energy. The result? Foods brown and cook evenly and fast while retaining their natural moisture."

Advantium combines a speed cook oven, convection oven, sensor microwave oven and warming proofing oven all in one. Imagine cooking food in anywhere from half to three-quarters of the time it would normally take with a convection oven vs. the issues involved with microwave cooking. The issue as to why this technology is not in everyone's home is a simple one: price. As with any new technology, research and development get paid for by the first adopters who are either wealthy or just have to have the latest and greatest and are willing to pay the price. The issue is, this is not a new smartphone that gets changed out every two years, and with new house sales declining, it seems that this technology is destined to stay in the homes of the rich and famous.

While I am sure this technology will start to become more mainstream, let's focus on the future and exciting new possibilities that GE believes will shape how we live.

Coming back to Maria and Roberto, GE imagines how food is grown, delivered and prepared, medicine is delivered and monitored and how we can better connect through everything from our smartphones to our furniture. Items not identified with the Maria and Roberto personas but other personas that GE created to address additional technologies that will have huge value to baby boomers.

They are:

- 3D food printer
- Induction units
- Smart faucet
- Laundry and clothing storage

Paul states that GE has not only worked with ADA guidelines but also Universal Design for their aging-in-place vision. They have engaged in the use of empathetic tools such as sight. Paul explains, "We have a lot of small, little graphics. How do we approach that? One is arthritis, obviously being able to turn the knobs, open the doors, just simple things like that. The other is reaching up very high or having to get on a step stool. If we design the kitchen from a holistic standpoint, how do you bring things down more into say the nose, top of the head to the waist areas? Picking up heavier loads, that's another issue. We are looking at the big picture. Obviously, we are not going to be able to solve every problem. We are going to tick off as many as we can."

These are GE's more near-term concerns vs. the 2025 product. They found through their ergonomic studies that seniors can't bend over and get in the back of a dishwasher, or get in the back of a laundry machine. They are trying to help seniors achieve their goals around cooking and cleaning to stay independent longer.

One of the largest concerns for aging staying in your home is cooking and forgetting to turn the stove off. GE has this issue front and center on their radar. Paul states, "We have a couple of ideas around if you think of a sensor over a stove to where it'll actually have some sort of smoke detector in it that will, if it starts smoking or the heat builds up too high, somebody just leaves it on, automatically shut off the system. That's one idea. Another one is real light... we have a couple of stoves with light bars over the handle, and those are out now to where they can notify people when things are done. The other is sound. It is obviously a big issue if you lose your hearing; you don't want a siren going off. That's a little bit of a tricky one. What we are doing is exploring, as this generation of baby boomers will move into the last part of their lives, and some of them are really tech-savvy and some of them are still not."

Paul does not feel it's realistic to think that we can just push all of these notifications to smartphones, as some just won't be that tech-savvy at the point they need help.

One of the other factors that GE is taking seriously is the need to downsize: making appliances the right size for the situation vs. a one-size-fits-all methodology. The challenge is that smaller used to be perceived as lower quality. Think of an apartment-sized refrigerator, 22 inches wide, vs. a 48-inch-wide GE Monogram side-by-side refrigerator. GE believes that while baby boomers will downsize to smaller spaces, they will not give up on quality. It seems we are finally hitting the issues that space-tight countries such as Japan and Europe have been dealing with for decades. How do we not give up on quality and services, yet make our spaces more flexible and functional?

*One of GE's micro-kitchen concepts – dubbed the monoblock – is an integrated unit with cooking, dishwashing, and refrigeration in a single standalone enclosure that would become a seamless part of the cabinetry.*

GE's press release for FirstBuilt states, "Boomers will have a huge impact on smaller living and it is GE's bet that they won't want to lose any of the luxury or convenience they've had in their lives,' said Lenzi. 'Whether they need a micro kitchen for their downsized dwelling, vacation home, refurbished man cave or boat . . . Boomers have always wanted the best."

In developing what would be the ideal smart kitchen, GE utilized the concept of crowdsourcing that was detailed out in a previous chapter. They basically built a micro-factory called FirstBuild and then engaged a co-creation social media community to help them design the first prototypes.

"Through FirstBuild and its global online community, GE Appliances is able to create, design, build and sell new innovations for your home faster than ever before," says Venkat Venkatakrishnan, director of R&D for GE Appliances and mentor for FirstBuild. "We launched a **micro-kitchen challenge** in May, and everyone from enthusiasts to experts can join FirstBuild.com to contribute their ideas to make the concepts a reality."

Who better than your clients to help you design and develop the product they will eventually buy? As my mentor, Dan Sullivan of Strategic Coach says, "Always test your ideas out on check-writers." It seems that GE has done just that. Concepts range from putting nice cabinetry doors on the front of washers and ventless dryers so that they can be in open view, eliminating the need for a laundry room or the awkwardness of having a stackable in a closet that is sandwiched behind cheap bifold doors, to a "monoblock," which is an entire kitchen in a single standalone unit that looks like cabinets.

One of the more applicable future technologies GE has involves laundry. Imagine washing, drying and storing clothes in a single unit. While GE's concept of an all-in-one washer and dryer has been around for years, the storage component of clothing due to fabric being compressed into a pellet makes this the perfect fit for a senior.

I have used a Korean all-in-one washer and dryer for over 12 years at a lake house. It has one opening and you place the clothes in and then it washes and then dries them, all in one space. It seems to take quite a bit more time per load because the activities are combined. It works great for beach towels and to set and not having to worry about switching the load so it won't get mildewed. While the all-in-one washer and dryer would be perfect for a senior doing one load a day at the most, I can't see this working for a family with kids as you are not able to multitask and handle large quantities of clothing.

GE's vision is that of that this type of laundry application would take up less room and add more convenience. According to Paul Hanley, "It came from the idea that, if you've ever been to a sporting event where they shoot those tightly packed T-shirts out at people." It's interesting how simple things can spark the creativity that will create a new invention. This is only now possible due to new technology in wrinkle-free fabrics. The implications for downsizing, travel, or senior living are immense...

Imagine for a moment that your seasonal clothing would fit into a shoebox! One of the largest obstacles for downsizing is the lack of storage space. This could reduce the size of a closet by 50 to 75 percent, which would free space up for the room and allow you to not have to choose what clothes you will have to get rid of, which can be a very dramatic event.

Let's develop this further: think of towels and linens taking up 75 percent less space in your home. Mind-blowing, isn't it!

**Laundry Pellets**

After washing and drying your clothing, the laundry machine in GE's Home 2025 compresses items into pellets and stores them in the machine. When ready to select your outfit, the machine dispenses the items in either pellet form for on-the-go or in revived form to wear now.

This is really not new technology, as much as it would be applied in a more commercialized format that is easier to use. The home shopping networks made mainstream the vacuum-seal bags for clothing that allow you to place your clothes and bedding into a plastic bag and then suck the air out and then seal so that you can get **triple** your storage space. At the very least, senior living should be utilizing this basic technology for their residents to help them manage their space easier.

**Smart Faucet with Hydration Sensor**

The smart faucet in GE's Home 2025 not only dispenses filtered water, but also ice and carbonated water, vitamins and various beverages. Just place your finger on the faucet and the built-in hydration sensor lets you instantly see your hydration level.

GE's smart faucet envisions that not only would your faucet properly filter your water, but it would also be able to read how hydrated you were and if you needed vitamins, etc., added for optimum health.

**Medical Dispenser**

No need to remember what medications to take when living in GE's Home 2025. Just place your hand on the mirror, and the Medical Dispenser reads your vital signs and decides the amount of medication needed for the day. The machine combines, processes and dispenses the medication in liquid form. Medication cartridges can be easily reloaded.

The fact is that with Google currently developing health-sensing technology such as a "diabetic contact lens" that can read your glucose levels through your tears and the XPRIZE's Qualcomm Tricorder contest that has announced its final 10 teams to build the world's first handheld smartphone medical diagnostic tool that can take vitals as well as oxygen saturation, it's not too hard to imagine that by placing a finger on the faucet sensor, your hydration levels and vitamin and mineral levels could be accessed. Having reservoirs of vitamins and minerals hidden under the sink, you could add them to your drink (no different than adding drops of vanilla to a recipe) along with flavoring if needed or desired.

Taking this concept one step further, GE has reimagined the medicine cabinet to be a combination of the GE imagined faucet and the Qualcomm Tricorder diagnostic tool!

Just imagine placing your hand on the mirror so that it recognizes you and takes your vitals, which are then sent to your doctor, or your loved one doing this to see if they need monitoring or if something is not as it should be. The medicine cabinet would then dispense the medications you need in liquid form through the sink. Medication cartridges would be easy to change and medication compliance would be much easier to monitor with constant vitals being taken. No need to be reminded to take this or that; it's all there for you.

Of course, if Roberto dumps his meds down the sink or won't place his hand on the cabinet, you could get a notification of this also.

The best way to imagine this is as a very sophisticated vending machine of sorts. The key will be monitoring the vitals to ensure medication compliance. Taking too many meds due to forgetting what you have already taken would be a thing of the past.

Paul Hanley feels this is more than plausible and not far out. He states, "As we went through our research we found medicine is gigantic and only growing, and how much medicine these seniors are taking is enormous. Whether they need them or not, the idea was instead of having to remember all that, you don't have to worry as much. It's a little bit of a different paradigm, where the senior says it's OK because I'm going to get up in the morning, I brush my teeth, I'm by my mirror, it dispenses ... it's a smart dispenser. It dispenses for that day in something I drink right there instead of sitting there on the counter. My mom has one of those Monday, Wednesday, Friday pill things that never seems to work and she dumps them out all over the place, but this would be taking a different look at the issue." The burden would be placed on the technology vs. the senior, with built-in reminders and safety features to ensure the best results.

Paul's mother is not alone. If you're over 50, you can

identify with trying to manage your prescriptions and supplements. It's easy to forget what you took when, especially when so many of these pills look alike, and then we take them out of their containers and unless we are highly organized and disciplined, we overtake or undertake weekly.

Induction Cooking

Packed in a 27-inch-wide design, the oven in GE's Home 2025 exhibit combines the efficiency of an induction cooktop, Advantium® Speedcook oven, sensor cooking, and a traditional thermal oven into a single unit. The interchangeable and integrated induction accessories allow for unlimited and exciting culinary exploration, as well as more cabinet space when stored in the integrated storage drawer below.

Induction cooking has been around since 1900, but not used by consumers until the 1970s through Westinghouse. Senior living, but especially memory care neighborhoods, have been utilizing induction units for safety and to be able to provide a more home-style dining experience than using steam tables as seen in a skilled nursing facility or cafeteria.

For those not familiar with the basics of an induction cooking unit, I have referenced Wikipedia:

**Induction cooking** heats a **cooking vessel by electrical induction**, instead of by **thermal conduction** from a flame, or an electrical **heating element**. For nearly all models of induction cooktops, a cooking vessel must be made of or contain a **ferromagnetic** metal such as cast iron or stainless steel. Copper, glass, and aluminum vessels can be placed on a ferromagnetic interface disk which functions as a conventional hotplate. According to the **U.S. Department of Energy**, the efficiency of energy transfer for an induction cooker is 84%, versus 74% for a smooth-top non-induction electrical unit and an approximate 40% for a gas cooktop.

So why does GE see this as a future technology? Paul Hanely explains that while this is not a new technology, it hasn't caught on. "Partially due to Americans' love of cooking with gas; another issue is the lack of understanding and thinking that it's radiating the food. The final is it requires new cookware."

The benefits of induction cooking are immense.

- The obvious benefit is the energy savings.
- Seniors and senior living have the ability to safely cook and then remove the pan or cookware and the surface is safe to touch.
- Homestyle cooking can be performed in a safe environment that is non-institutional and eliminates the need for steam wells.
- When the induction units are mounted under a granite surface, the space looks just like a regular counter when not in use and therefore can be

placed on an island and not hurt the aesthetics of the space.

- Finally, the countertop where induction cooking takes place can be dual purpose. Space is always limited, whether in an apartment or performance kitchen, so being able to utilize the cooktop space as a prep area or serving space when not in use allows the countertop to be more flexible.

With all of these benefits, we still see both existing senior living environments and new-build homes miss the return on investment that induction cooking units provide. It's amazing to see a $17 million project value engineer out the induction units because they will have to buy more expensive pots. Silly, I know, but it happens every day.

**Thermal Nightstand**

In GE's Home 2025, a thermoelectric nano material allows a user to activate a designated area on the nightstand using their body heat, such as from a finger, and leave a reminder. The thermoelectric nano material also recognizes the temperature difference between the surface and any object you set on it, such as a cup of coffee, and will adjust to keep your beverage warm (or cool).

While I love the idea of smart furniture and Corning Glass, "Day in the Life" video makes a hard case for all of our surfaces becoming interactive computer screens, this nightstand seemed a bit out there. Think of a digital Etch A Sketch that's able to warm or cool your drink and know which one it should do.

GE assures me that this is not so out-of-the-real as both the thermoelectric nanotechnology exists, as well as the heating and cooling technology. It's the combining of these technologies that will take some time.

Being able to leave notes for a loved one or resident to start their day off with a smile or reminder is a wonderful idea. Corning would also have this surface light up and become the alarm clock.

Under Cabinet Mounted 3D Printer
GE's home 2025 comes equipped with an undercabinet mounted 3D printer where homeowners can conveniently print their own housewares, home dishes and toy toys.

Roberto gets a notification that his meal is ready, it will stay hot and fresh for 8 hours.

The GE future kitchen has everything from ultra-smart appliances (something out of *The Jetsons*) to the induction cooktop technology that has been used by the public since the 1970s. The key is that the appliances are integrated into your food delivery system, your smartphone technology, and 3D printing.

If anyone is familiar with PeaPod (mostly in large cities), which started in 1990, it delivers groceries to your door from your online order for a nominal fee. GE envisions the future kitchen as a step up from this, having the appliances have storage units, similar to a freezer case in the grocery store, that can be stocked from outside the house and accessed from inside the house. The stocking method would be completely secure and medications could be delivered this way as well. You would determine your basics and order them up and then meal-plan, and the appliance would calculate how much you needed of what for your recipes and servings and order the proper amounts. GE envisions you would possibly have a personal micro-garden to grow items that you enjoy growing yourself or are not available at your store.

The appliances would be a combo refrigerator/oven that would allow you to prep a meal for cooking (plate up), similar to a crock pot, and then start cooking at the appropriate time.

They also envision that leftovers could be utilized with a 3D food printer for pet treats. Although the technology is currently available to 3D print meat, they feel it will take some time for people to adapt to this technology.

The focus is on how can we have fresh food without it going bad when you're only cooking for one or two. The analogy was given of making tacos for one and the whole head of lettuce would go bad, as the persona only needed a small amount. Seniors tend to reduce cooking due to the issues of cooking for one with leftovers. If we could reduce this and engage cooking with interactive learning, the whole process would become enjoyable again.

In summary, Paul Hanely says, "Looking back, I think that one of the interesting things about this 2025 project was we were grounded in current technology or technology that's either pretty far developed or pretty far in it. We couldn't just say, your kitchen is going to float, or your clothes are going to automatically be clean by solar light, or some new element. Everything had to be grounded in a technology that we either A, know it's worked or B, is right there. I think that gave the designers a little bit more of a challenge, but I think you come out with better ideas when you do that kind of stuff.

So people aren't like, 'Yeah, hovercraft,' or whatever it is. I don't get it. This kind of stuff is out there. As I mentioned before, the little T-shirt things that they shoot out at sports games, our laundry concept uses that same technology.

We are living in the opposite world of you, by the way. That's why these projects are so fun for our designers. Our teams include industrial designers, user interface designers, UX and engineers and researchers, and our internal user insight team. It was good to stretch everybody's wings and see what's possible instead of trying to make the millionth dryer of the year."

In January of 2015, after this interview, GE unveiled smartphone appliances that let you do everything from preheating your oven to send a warning to you when your clothes have been left in the dryer too long and will wrinkle soon.

> We need not be afraid of the future, for the future will be in our own hands. – **Thomas E. Dewey**

# 17. Summary, Bonus and Resource Link

**Summary:**

*The Jetsons* aired in 1962 and was set in the future, 2062, they gave 100 years for this imagined world to become reality, yet it's only taken 53 years. While some of the technology on the show is not as mainstream today as others (flying cars), we can expect that as the past 10 years have felt like technology was created at light speed, the next 10 will fundamentally change how we all live.

We have discussed technology that can help the blind to see, the deaf to hear and the disabled to walk again. Self-driving vehicles and other mobility devices that increase our freedom and safety. Lighting that has become interactive and aides in our wellbeing as well as the planets. Crowdsourcing and gamification that can help to complete simple tasks to complex tasks by leveraging our connection to others through the internet.

Behavior modification through gamification can make you physically and mentally healthier, increase the compliance of your team and residents or save lives. Robots that reduce stress on caregiver's bodies, engage with residents or deliver their medications via drone.

While data mining and artificial intelligence run as a part of most of the technologies presented, they deserve their individual kudos for diagnosing medical conditions and helping to learn our behavior and patterns so that we are not inundated with information that is not relevant to us.

We have been introduced to 3D printing that will change how our goods are delivered to us similar to having a computer and printer in your home. 3D printing will also increase the dignity we can provide for our residents by appealing to the look of food not just the taste without causing a choking issue.

Finally, we looked into the future with GE's 2025 Home and saw how the need for clothing storage could be substantially reduced and furniture and appliances becoming dynamically integrated with technology will help us stay in their homes longer.

Some future technologies to think about that we have not covered in this book but have interesting implications are, LED lite highways, a breathalyzer that can detect disease, nanotechnology, virtual reality, We:eX Navigate Jacket and Corning's Day in the Life video which features how important glass will be in the application of technology in our surroundings.

**Bonus:**

As part of a group called Abundance 360 that Peter

Diamandis runs, I get access to not only the top technology geniuses in the world but also Peter's brain. He is truly one of the great thinkers of our day and freely shares his knowledge with all. While not all of these may apply, I hope you will find it as thought-provoking and exciting as I have. Enjoy!

Peter Diamandis, Founder of the XPRIZE – **Proof We Are Living in 2019**

**Communications Abundance:** We are living in a time where there will be no person disconnected. Everyone will have access to the world's information. We have seen Facebook and Microsoft wire the entire globe. 5G networks have begun deployment allowing us to download movies in seconds rather than minutes. In 2017, about 3.8 billion people were connected. That's half of the world's population. In the next 5 to 6 years, it will be the entire world at even faster speeds which means doubling the consumer base for businesses and spreading information to everyone as quickly as possible.

**Cryptocurrencies:** In 2017 we saw a 5,000 percent increase in the cryptocurrency marketplace hitting $800 billion units way to a trillion dollars in 2018. From Bitcoin to Ethereum and Coinbase. These companies sell tokens to raise capital in large amounts. Try $6.4 billion in 2016 and 2017. Institutions are starting to invest which only validates further the direction of cryptocurrency and its effect on the world marketplace. It's growing too fast to ignore and soon, numerous businesses like UPS are going to partake. Even Estonia has used this new borderless currency to create their own E-Residency program.

**Energy Abundance:** Our energy innovation is at an all-time high. We are constantly setting records for energy creation from renewable sources. The cost of coal is 5 to 6 cents per kilowatt hour but solar energy in Mexico is at 2.7 cents. That's a big difference in electricity bills for not just families, but entire countries. Coastlines of various countries, like Scotland, are turning into wind farms that supply power to homes. Costa Rica went 300 days in a row with 100 percent renewable energy. Even a cloudy Germany was able to do 33 percent for the entire year. We are going to have so much energy production in the next few years, we won't need petroleum or coal to create that anymore. Even car companies see the wave and are investing in batteries to make more cars electric by 2022. The energy world as we know is shifting and doing it quickly.

**Healthcare Abundance:** Healthcare is finding advances in all kinds of areas to help with the diagnosis of disease to sequencing genomes to help people stay healthier. The Tricorder XPRIZE winners created a handheld mobile device that can diagnose 15 diseases on the spot. This puts more power into our hands to be able to help ourselves. We are starting to use technology such as

Abilify that utilizes sensors to tell whether you are compliant with your medication and can even warn your doctor when you aren't. The real ticket is being able to sequence your own DNA and even that of food you're eating to know exactly what is going on inside of your body. CRISPR is a software that allows us to accurately and easily change nucleotide sequences in our DNA that could decrease our chances for diseases.

**Transportation Abundance:** In 2018, we saw the autonomous car happen. We saw test runs and videos and in many cities, you can ride in an autonomous car right now. Uber announced a 24,000 car deal with Volvo with cars operational by 2019. These are cars with steering wheels, gas pedals, or brake pedals. Just an onboard computer that gets you where you need to go. This will make the biggest difference in the world in countries and cities like Sao Paulo and Mexico City and China. It's going to completely change the truck driving game. Today, it's about giving the truck driver a break and not falling asleep at the wheel. Next, it's a fleet of trucks without human drivers. And the next step is coming from places like Airbus and Boeing creating the air taxi business. Uber Elevate is going to be taking over parking garages near you sooner than you think. Not to mention we have the Hyperloop that can connect entire cities and maybe rocket travel in the near future as well. Soon, it will be so easy to see the world or get from one place to another in minutes.

**Robotics and Drones:** Robots are becoming a part of everything we do and making life easier. We spend so much money as our aging parents go to old age homes. $80,000 a year is the average. Imagine if you can have a robot that gives them the dignity to stay in their own home, helps them get up, make their meals, go to the bathroom. We're starting to see robotics in farming and construction. In New York, LA, Seattle, we're seeing Amazon go open up a store without any employees. The AI knows who you are and what you took and charges your Amazon account when you leave. Drones are being utilized to do anything from forecasting the weather to planting trees in deforested areas.

**AI and Computation:** We are seeing a vast improvement in AI across different dimensions of our lives. AlphaGo Zero is a computer program that has taught itself how to play the game Go. The original AlphaGo defeated the top ranked player in the world 4 to 1. AlphaGo Zero beat that program 100-0. It learns completely from its own experience and continues to play itself to get better. We have AI programming that can do facial recognition while you are moving. In the future this could mean you walk into a store, they see you coming in and no exactly who you are, what you are likely to be looking for and what questions you might ask. There are new virtual desk assistants from Google and Soul Machines that are able to hold conversations. AI is helping us predict difficulties and mental and physical health from suicidality to heart failure.

**Space and Physics:** You can put a deposit down for a flight on Blue Origin and New Shepard, suborbital flights that goes up and flies back down. SpaceX had 15 consecutive landings of their first stage rocket. Something that 2 years ago people said could not be done is now a routine. The Kennedy Space Center has Falcon Heavy ready for launch to take astronauts to the moon and with plans for humans on the surface of Mars by 2024! Even with these steps, we have seen so much more of our universe. We discovered a solar system reasonably close to our home with seven earth like planets. We have seen early signs of life on Saturn! The Logo Observatory witness colliding neutron stars and scientists discovered massive binary black holes. This is truly the days of science fiction.

I want you to feel how fast things are going. My goal, the water is boiling it's getting hotter and hotter and a lot of us are focused on our businesses, focused on our customers, focused on our kids and our family and we lose track of how fast it's going. I don't want you blindsided. And so my goal here is to give you a sense of what I'm seeing as the trends. You should walk away with like, there's real stuff happening here. I need to pay more attention to it. Not all of it. Pick one or two things that's important for your future, for your investments, for your life.

Check out www.LisaMCini.com for resource links.

71593720R00230

Made in the
USA
Middletown, DE